curriculum mathematics practice 4

Ruthish School

C Oliver   **A Ledsham**   **R Elvin**   **M Bindley**

Oxford University Press

Oxford University Press, Great Clarendon Street, Oxford OX2 6DP

Oxford   New York
Athens   Auckland   Bangkok   Bogota   Bombay
Buenos Aires   Calcutta   Cape Town   Dar es Salaam
Delhi   Florence   Hong Kong   Istanbul   Karachi
Kuala Lumpur   Madras   Madrid   Melbourne
Mexico City   Nairobi   Paris   Singapore
Taipei   Tokyo   Toronto   Warsaw

and associated companies in

Berlin   Ibadan

Oxford is a trade mark of Oxford University Press
© Oxford University Press 1996

Series first published as *Comprehensive Mathematics Practice* 1981
Updated edition of *Curriculum Mathematics Practice* first published 1996
Reprinted 1998

ISBN 0 19 833744 2
A CIP record for this book is available from the British Library.

Typeset and illustrated by Tech Set Ltd
Printed and bound in Great Britain by Butler and Tanner Ltd, Frome and London

Preface

Curriculum Mathematics Practice is an updated version of *Comprehensive Mathematics Practice*, a successful series designed for the majority of students in their first years of secondary schooling. As before, the books provide a vast range of carefully constructed and graded exercises in a coherent mathematical progression, with many of these exercises set in a real-life context. The levels targeted are 3–8, and details of how all six new books relate to the curriculum are given in the Answer Book.

These new books do not attempt to provide a complete scheme for the National Curriculum. No attempt has been made for instance to cover 'Using and Applying Mathematics' or computer work. It is expected, however, that mathematics departments will use other resources for those aspects (e.g. *Oxford Mathematics*) and that *Curriculum Mathematics Practice* will provide a core of skill practice within an overall scheme of work.

The series has the same objective as the original books. The series should enable students 'to gain confidence in their abilities and master the fundamental processes so necessary for future success'.

Mark Bindley
Revising Editor
December 1995

Contents

Unit 1   Ratio

A *ratio* is used when we wish to compare two or more quantities.

'Filla' is a powder that is mixed with water to form a paste.
The powder and the water are mixed together in the ratio 3:1. We say that the *ratio* is 'three to one' or simply '3 to 1' or 3:1.

Ratio is a convenient way to compare quantities, but the quantities *must* be given in the *same* units.

Any quantity of mixed 'Filla' paste will consist of 3 parts powder and 1 part water.

This is the same as saying that the *fraction* of water in the mixed paste is $\frac{1}{4}$.
Fractions compare the parts into which an object is divided with the *whole object*.
Ratios compare the parts into which an object is divided with *each other*.

Ratios can be simplified like fractions by dividing by a common factor.

Example 1

Give each ratio in its simplest form.

a 6:8   **b** £1.50:£5.00

a 6 and 8 have a common factor of 2 so, dividing by 2 gives

$$6:8 = 3:4$$

b Changing to pennies and then dividing by the common factor of 50 gives

$$£1.50:£5.00 = 150:500$$
$$= 3:10$$

Exercise 1.1

Give each ratio in its simplest form.

1 8:10	**2** 10:12
3 6:16	**4** 10:16
5 2:4	**6** 9:12
7 12:15	**8** 15:24
9 27:30	**10** 3:9
11 8:12	**12** 16:20
13 36:40	**14** 10:15
15 15:20	**16** 10:25
17 25:40	**18** 5:25
19 18:30	**20** 30:36
21 30:48	**22** 24:40
23 56:64	**24** 18:27
25 36:45	**26** £1.50:£2.00
27 £1.20:£2.00	**28** £1.60:£4.00
29 £2.50:£4.00	**30** £1.20:£6.00
31 £2.50:£10.00	**32** £1.50:£9.00
33 £0.80:£2.00	**34** £0.90:£3.00
35 £0.50:£2.00	**36** 1 m 60 cm:2 m
37 2 m 40 cm:3 m	**38** 4 m 50 cm:6 m
39 4 m 80 cm:8 m	**40** 1 m 50 cm:4 m
41 4 m 50 cm:9 m	**42** 60 cm:2 m
43 50 cm:3 m	**44** 1 cm 8 mm:2 cm
45 3 cm 2 mm:4 cm	**46** 7 cm 5 mm:10 cm
47 2 cm 5 mm:3 cm	**48** 1 cm 5 mm:6 cm
49 5 mm:4 cm	**50** 6 mm:3 cm

Example 2

In a 50-seater bus, there are 16 seats for smokers. Find the ratio of seats for smokers to those for non-smokers.

No. of seats for smokers = 16

So no. of seats for non-smokers = 50 − 16 = 34

Therefore the ratio is 16:34 or 8:17

Exercise 1.2

1 On a supermarket shelf there are 6 bags of plain flour and 9 bags of self-raising flour.
Find the ratio of plain flour to self-raising flour.
2 Anne weighs 28 kg and Jandeep weighs 40 kg.
Find the ratio of Anne's weight to Jandeep's.
3 At a party, 24 children asked for tea and 30 asked for lemonade.
Find the ratio of those who had tea to those who had lemonade.

4 Jack has 21 marbles and Tom has 28.
Find the ratio of the number of Jack's marbles to those of Tom.

5 Kirsty has picked 27 flowers and Melanie has picked 45.
Find the ratio of the number that Kirsty has picked to those of Melanie.

6 Liam is 96 cm tall and Robert is 120 cm tall.
Find the ratio of Liam's height to Robert's.

7 In a class of 30 pupils there are 12 boys. Find the ratio of boys to girls.

8 In the bread shop there are 20 loaves on the shelf; 5 of them are brown and the rest are white loaves.
Find the ratio of brown loaves to white loaves.

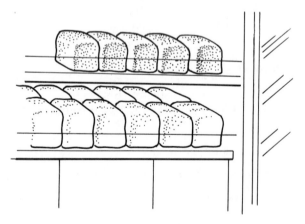

9 A farmer has a flock of 60 sheep; 12 of them are black and the rest are white.
Find the ratio of black sheep to white sheep.

10 A railway carriage has 56 seats and 24 of them are for first-class passengers.
Find the ratio of first-class seats to second-class seats.

If a quantity is to be shared between 2 people so that one gets twice as much as the other, it is shared in the ration 2 : 1.

Example 3

Share

a £45 in the ratio 2 : 1
b 90 litres in the ratio 4 : 5 : 6

a Total number of shares $= 2 + 1 = 3$

therefore one share $= £45 \div 3 = £15$

therefore the value of the first share
$= £15 \times 2$
$= £30$

and the value of the second share
$= £15 \times 1$
$= £15$

Therefore the two amounts are £30 and £15.

Check that these two shares total £45.

b Total number of shares $= 4 + 5 + 6 = 15$

therefore one share $= (90 \div 15)$ litres
$= 6$ litres

therefore the first share $= (6 \times 4)$ litres
$= 24$ litres

the second share $= (6 \times 5)$ litres
$= 30$ litres

and the third share $= (6 \times 6)$ litres
$= 36$ litres

Therefore the three amounts are 24, 30 and 36 litres.

Check that these three shares total 90 litres.

Exercise 1.3

1 Share £48 in the ratio 2 : 1.
2 Share £60 in the ratio 3 : 1.
3 Share £80 in the ratio 4 : 1.
4 Share £91 in the ratio 6 : 1.
5 Share £70 in the ratio 3 : 2.
6 Share £120 in the ratio 5 : 3.

7 Share 112 ml of milk between the cat and her
  kitten in the ratio 4 : 3.

8 Share 162 ml of milk between the cat and the dog
  in the ratio 4 : 5.

9 Share 200 g of sweets between Aisha and Nicola
  in the ratio 3 : 5.

10 Share 120 g of cereal between Waseem and David
  in the ratio 3 : 7.

---

11 Share £108 in the ratio 3 : 2 : 1.

12 Share £144 in the ratio 5 : 3 : 1.

13 Share £135 in the ratio 4 : 3 : 2.

14 Share £180 in the ratio 6 : 5 : 1.

15 Share £300 in the ratio 6 : 5 : 4.

16 Share 315 g of flour between Mrs Smith, Mrs
  Johnson and Mrs Bates in the ratio 4 : 2 : 1.

17 Share 450 kg of soil between three gardeners in
  the ratio 4 : 5 : 6.

18 Share 1500 ml of paraffin between Mr Brown, Mr
  Jones and Mr Patel in the ratio 2 : 3 : 5.

19 A bottle containing 560 ml of lemonade exactly
  fills three glasses belonging to Jill, Jane and Paul.
  If the capacities of the glasses are in the ratio of
  3 : 5 : 6, how much lemonade does each child
  receive?

PAUL   JANE   JILL

20 A teacher shares out 50 sheets of paper between
  three pupils in the ratio 6 : 9 : 10.
  How many sheets does each pupil receive?

Example 4

A sum of money is shared in the ratio 2 : 3.
If the smaller share is 50 p, what is the larger
share?

    50 p is equal to 2 shares
so 25 p is equal to 1 share

therefore the larger share = 25 p × 3 = 75 p

Check that the two shares are in the ratio 2 : 3.

Exercise 1.4

1 A sum of money is shared in the ratio 2 : 3.
  If the smaller share is 30 p, what is the larger
  share?
2 A sum of money is shared in the ratio 2 : 5.
  If the smaller share is 16 p, what is the larger
  share?
3 A sum of money is shared in the ratio 4 : 5.
  If the smaller share is 36 p, what is the larger
  share?
  How much money was shared out?
4 A sum of money is shared in the ratio 3 : 7.
  If the smaller share is £12, what is the larger
  share?
  How much money was shared out?
5 A sum of money is shared in the ratio 5 : 8.
  If the smaller share is £20, what is the larger
  share?
  How much money was shared out?
6 A sum of money is shared out in the ratio 2 : 3 : 5.
  If the smallest share is £10, what are the other
  two shares?

7 A sum of money is shared out in the ratio 3 : 5 : 7. If the smallest share is £9, what are the other two shares?

8 A sum of money is shared out in the ratio 5 : 6 : 9. If the smallest share is 25 p, what are the other two shares?
How much money was shared out altogether?

9 At a bread shop the prices of a white and a brown loaf are in the ratio of 5 : 6.
If a white loaf costs 30 p, what is the price of a brown loaf?

10 The heights of two sisters Lynn and Sophie are in the ratio of 4 : 5.
If Lynn is 120 cm tall, how tall is Sophie?

11 The weights of two brothers Martin and Richard are in the ratio of 3 : 4.
If Martin's weight is 45 kg, how much does Richard weigh?

12 A thermos flask can exactly fill two cups whose capacities are in the ratio of 3 : 5.
If the smaller one has a capacity of 150 ml, what is the capacity of the larger one?
What is the capacity of the flask?

13 In class 3A the ratio of boys to girls is 6 : 7.
If there are 12 boys in the class, find
   a the number of girls in the class and
   b the number of pupils in the class altogether.

14 A long, thin piece of wood is cut into two pieces, the ratio of whose lengths is 9 : 11.
If the shorter piece is 45 cm long, what is the length of the longer piece?
What was the length of the original piece?

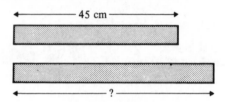

15 Some sweets are shared between Tom, Luke and Kim in the ratio 2 : 3 : 4.
If Tom has 100 g, what weight has
   a Luke
   b Kim?
What total weight of sweets is shared out?

16 The boys in class 4B have three sports options: cross-country, rugby and football.
If they choose in the respective ratio 2 : 5 : 8 and 4 choose cross-country, how many choose
   a rugby
   b football?
How many boys are there in the class altogether?

17 The girls in class 5A have three sports options: squash, netball and hockey.
If they choose in the respective ratio 3 : 4 : 7 and 6 choose squash, how many choose
   a netball
   b hockey?
How many girls are there in the class altogether?

18 A sum of money is shared in the ratio 5 : 3.
If 30 p is the larger share, what is the smaller share?

19 A sum of money is shared in the ratio 7 : 2.
If £28 is the larger share, what is the smaller share?
How much money is shared out?

20 The ages of two sisters Alice and Emma are in the ratio of 3 : 2.
If Alice is 12 years old, how old is Emma?

Example 5

a If 3 kg of apples cost 99 p, what would 5 kg cost?

b If 12 eggs cost 60 p, how many eggs could be bought for 45 p?

a If 3 kg of apples cost 99 p,
then 1 kg of apples cost $99 \div 3 = 33$ p
therefore 5 kg costs $33 \times 5 = 165$ p $= £1.65$

b If 12 eggs cost 60 p,
then 1 egg costs $60 \div 12 = 5$ p
therefore the number of eggs for 45 p is
$45 \div 5 = 9$.

Exercise 1.5

1 If 5 kg of potatoes cost 90 p, what is the cost of 3 kg?

2 If 6 litres of paraffin cost 96 p, what is the cost of 4 litres?

3 If 20 postcards cost 180 p, what is the cost of 50?

4 If it takes me 45 minutes to walk 5 km, how long will it take me to walk
   a 9 km
   b 4 km?

5 If 12 m² of carpet cost £60, find the cost of
   a 5 m²
   b 8 m².

6 If 5 kg of bananas cost £2.40, find the cost of 2 kg.

7 If 4 kg of tomatoes cost £3.60, find the cost of 3 kg.

8 If 6 kg of apples cost £1.92, find the cost of
   a 4 kg
   b 5 kg.

9 If 5 kg of pears cost £1.80, find the cost of
   a 3 kg
   b 4 kg.

10 If 5 m of curtain track cost £12, find the cost of
   a 3 m
   b 8 m.

11 If 5 m of dress fabric cost £14, find the cost of
   a 4 m
   b 12 m.

12 If 10 m of a certain kind of electric cable cost £5, find the cost of
   a 3 m
   b 7 m.

13 If 10 m² of vinyl flooring cost £12, find the cost of
   a 3 m²
   b 8 m²
   c 12 m².

14 If 10 tonnes of garden soil cost £75, find the cost of
   a 3 tonnes
   b 4 tonnes
   c 12 tonnes.

15 If 20 litres of petrol cost £10 find the cost of
   a 8 litres,
   b 12 litres
   c 30 litres.

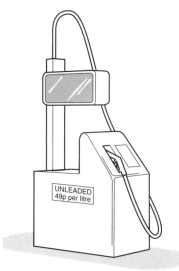

16 If 8 oranges cost 96 p, how many can be bought for 60 p?

17 If 5 grapefruits cost 80 p, how many can be bought for 48 p?

18 If 6 eggs cost 36 p, how many can be bought for 90 p?

19 If 5 bread buns cost 30 p, how many can be bought for
 a 18 p
 b 48 p?

20 If 5 doughnuts cost 60 p, how many can be bought for
 a 24 p
 b 84 p?

21 If 6 packets of crisps cost 96 p, how many packets can be bought for
 a 32 p
 b 80 p?

22 If 6 pencils cost 54 p, how many can be bought for
 a 36 p
 b 90 p?

23 If 12 birthday cards cost 84 p, how many can be bought for
 a 35 p
 b 56 p?

24 If 30 envelopes cost 60 p, how many can be bought for
 a 50 p
 b 90 p?

25 If 4 mini bars of chocolate cost 60 p, how many can be bought for
 a 45 p
 b £1.50?

26 If 5 calculator batteries cost £1.50, how many can be bought for
 a 90 p
 b £2.10?

27 If 10 small bars of soap cost £1.20, how many can be bought for
 a 48 p
 b 84 p
 c £1.08?

28 If 10 cans of lemonade cost £2, how many cans can be bought for
 a 60 p
 b £1.60
 c £2.80?

29 If 60 brass screws cost £1.80, how many can be bought for
 a 45 p
 b £1.50?

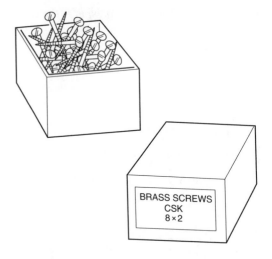

BRASS SCREWS
CSK
8×2

30 If 12 bathroom tiles cost £3.60, how many can be bought for
 a £2.40
 b £6?

Unit 2   Polygons

Parallel lines

Parallel lines are always the same distance apart. To show the lines that are parallel, arrow heads are placed on the lines.

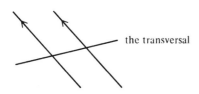

the transversal

A straight line that cuts parallel lines is called a *transversal*.

Reminder
Adjacent angles
The sum of two adjacent angles is 180°.

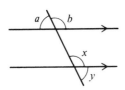

$\hat{a} + \hat{b} = 180°$ because these are adjacent angles.

$\hat{x} + \hat{y} = 180°$ because these are also adjacent angles.

Vertically opposite angles
Vertically opposite angles are equal.

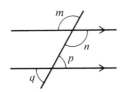

$\hat{m} = \hat{n}$ because these are vertically opposite angles.

$\hat{p} = \hat{q}$ because these are also vertically opposite angles.

Exercise 2.1

1 Which angle is
   a adjacent to $\hat{a}$
   b vertically opposite to $\hat{a}$
   c adjacent to $\hat{x}$
   d vertically opposite to $\hat{x}$?

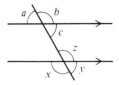

2 Which angle is
   a adjacent to $\hat{l}$
   b vertically opposite to $\hat{l}$
   c adjacent to $\hat{p}$
   d vertically opposite to $\hat{p}$?

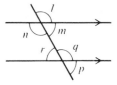

3 Which angle is
   a adjacent to $\hat{b}$
   b vertically opposite to $\hat{b}$
   c adjacent to $\hat{t}$
   d vertically opposite to $\hat{t}$?

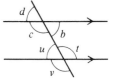

4 Which angle is
   a adjacent to $\hat{p}$
   b vertically opposite to $\hat{p}$
   c adjacent to $\hat{x}$
   d vertically opposite to $\hat{x}$?

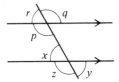

5 Which angle is
   a adjacent to $\hat{a}$
   b vertically opposite to $\hat{a}$
   c adjacent to $\hat{x}$
   d vertically opposite to $\hat{x}$?

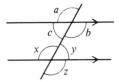

6 Which angle is
   a adjacent to $\hat{l}$
   b vertically opposite to $\hat{l}$
   c adjacent to $\hat{p}$
   d vertically opposite to $\hat{p}$?

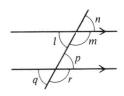

8

Alternate angles
Alternate angles are equal.

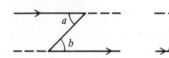

$\hat{a} = \hat{b}$ because they are alternate angles.

$\hat{x} = \hat{y}$ because they are alternate angles.

Exercise 2.2

1 Which angle is
   a alternate with $\hat{a}$
   b alternate with $\hat{b}$?

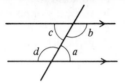

2 Which angle is
   a alternate with $\hat{p}$
   b alternate with $\hat{q}$?

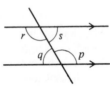

3 Which angle is
   a alternate with $\hat{k}$
   b alternate with $\hat{l}$?

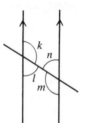

4 Which angle is
   a alternate with $\hat{a}$
   b alternate with $\hat{b}$?

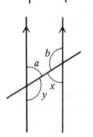

5 Which angle is
   a alternate with $\hat{l}$
   b alternate with $\hat{m}$?

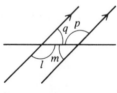

6 Which angle is
   a alternate with $\hat{u}$
   b alternate with $\hat{v}$?

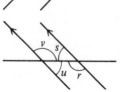

Example 1

Find a giving reasons.

As $\hat{a}$ and 80° are alternate angles
   $\hat{a} = 80°$

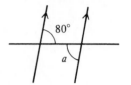

Example 2

Find $\hat{x}$ and $\hat{y}$ giving reasons.

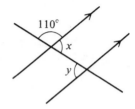

As $\hat{x}$ and 110° are adjacent angles,
   $\hat{x} = 180° - 110° = 70°$

As $\hat{x}$ and $\hat{y}$ are alternate angles,
   $\hat{x} = \hat{y} = 70°$

Exercise 2.3

Find each angle that is marked with a letter, giving reasons.

1

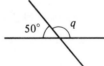

2

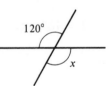

3

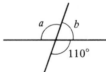

4

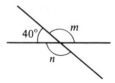

5

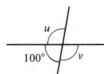

6

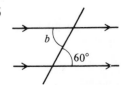

7

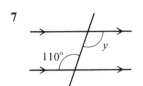

110° y

8

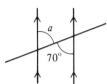

q
80°

9

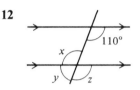

a
70°

10

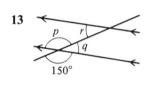

q
50°

11

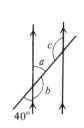

60°
a
b

12

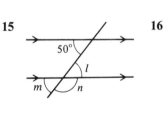

110°
x
y z

13

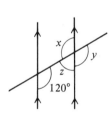

p r
q
150°

14

c
a
b
40°

15

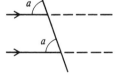

50°
l
m n

16

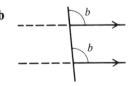

x
y
z
120°

Corresponding angles
Corresponding angles are equal.
Four examples are shown below.

a

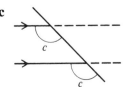

a
a

b

b
b

c

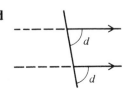

c
c

d

d
d

Exercise 2.4

1 Which angle is
  a corresponding to $\hat{a}$
  b corresponding to $\hat{b}$?

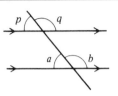

p q
a b

2 Which angle is
  a corresponding to $\hat{l}$
  b corresponding to $\hat{m}$?

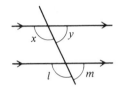

x y
l m

3 Which angle is
  a corresponding to $\hat{b}$
  b corresponding to $\hat{c}$?

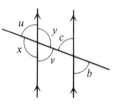

u y c
x
v
b

4 Which angle is
  a corresponding to $\hat{m}$
  b corresponding to $\hat{n}$?

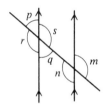

p
s
r
q m
n

5 Which angle is
  a corresponding to $\hat{a}$
  b corresponding to $\hat{b}$?

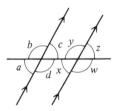

b c y z
a d x w

6 Which angle is
  a corresponding to $\hat{l}$
  b corresponding to $\hat{m}$?

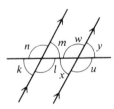

n m w y
k l x u

Example 3

Find $\hat{x}$ giving reasons.

As $\hat{x}$ and 110° are
corresponding angles,
    $\hat{x} = 110°$

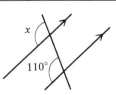

x
110°

Example 4

Find $\hat{a}$ and $\hat{b}$
giving reasons.

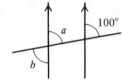

As $\hat{a}$ and 100° are
corresponding angles,
$\hat{a} = 100°$

As $\hat{a}$ and $\hat{b}$ are vertically opposite angles,
$\hat{a} = \hat{b} = 100°$

Exercise 2.5

Find each angle that is marked with a letter, giving
reasons.

1 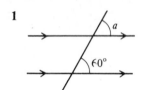 **2**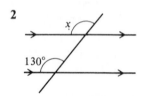

3 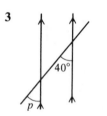 **4**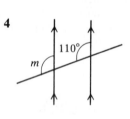

5 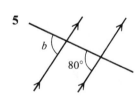 **6**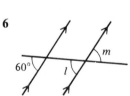

7 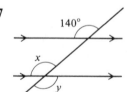 **8**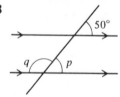

9 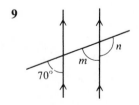 **10**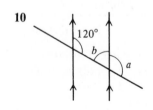

11 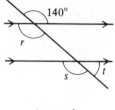 **12**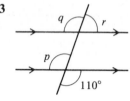

13 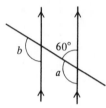 **14**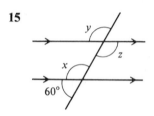

15 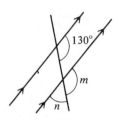 **16**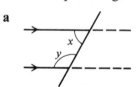

Allied angles
Allied angles are *supplementary*, i.e. the sum of
the two angles is 180°.
Two examples are given below.

a    **b**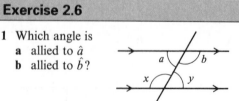

$$\hat{x} + \hat{y} = 180° \qquad \hat{a} + \hat{b} = 180°$$

Exercise 2.6

1 Which angle is
  a allied to $\hat{a}$
  b allied to $\hat{b}$?

2 Which angle is
  a allied to $\hat{l}$
  b allied to $\hat{m}$?

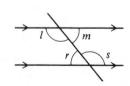

3 Which angle is
  a allied to $\hat{p}$
  b allied to $\hat{q}$?

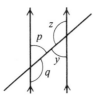

4 Which angle is
  a allied to $\hat{m}$
  b allied to $\hat{n}$?

5 Which angle is
  a allied to $\hat{a}$
  b allied to $\hat{b}$?

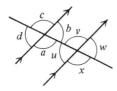

6 Which angle is
  a allied to $\hat{l}$
  b allied to $\hat{m}$?

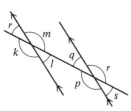

Example 5

Find $\hat{a}$ giving reasons.

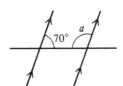

As $\hat{a}$ and 70° are
allied angles,
$$\hat{a} = 180° - 70°$$
$$= 110°$$

Example 6

Find $\hat{x}$ and $\hat{y}$
giving reasons.

As $\hat{x}$ and 100° are
allied angles,
$$\hat{x} = 180° - 100°$$
$$= 80°$$

As $\hat{x}$ and $\hat{y}$ are vertically opposite angles,

$$\hat{x} = \hat{y} = 80°$$

Exercise 2.7

Find each angle that is marked with a letter, giving reasons.

1

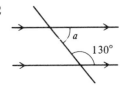

2

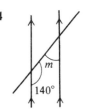

3

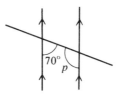

4

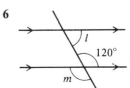

5

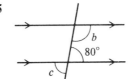

6

7

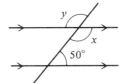

8

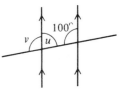

9

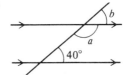

10

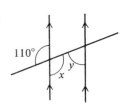

11

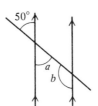

12

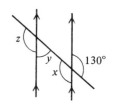

13

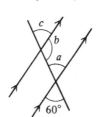

14

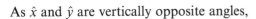

15

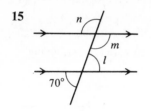

16

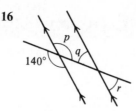

17

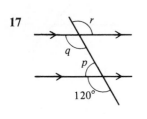

18

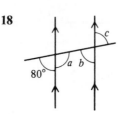

A *right-angled* isosceles triangle is a special isosceles triangle.

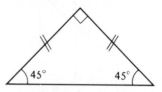

Its angles are 90°, 45°, and 45°.
A 45° set-square is an example of such a triangle.

The scalene triangle

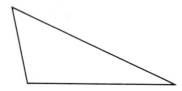

All sides are of different lengths.
All angles are of different size.
The scalene triangle has no symmetry.

Triangles

You should be familiar with acute-angled triangles, right-angled triangles and obtuse-angled triangles.
Here are three other types of triangles that you need to know.

The equilateral triangle

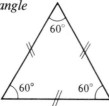

All three sides are equal in length.
All three angles are equal to 60°.
The equilateral triangle has three lines of symmetry, and also rotational symmetry.

The isosceles triangle

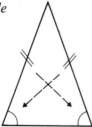

Two of the sides are equal in length.
The angles opposite the equal sides are equal.
The isosceles triangle has one line of symmetry, but no rotational symmetry.

Example 7

Describe each of the following triangles.

a

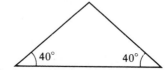

The sum of the angles in a triangle is 180°.
The missing angle is 180° − 40° − 40°
$$= 140° − 40°$$
$$= 100°$$

So the triangle is isosceles and obtuse-angled.

b

The sum of the angles in a triangle is 180°.
The missing angle is 180° − 110° − 20°
$$= 70° − 20°$$
$$= 50°$$

So the triangle is scalene and obtuse-angled.

c

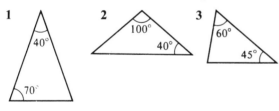

6 cm

6 cm

Two sides are both equal to 6 cm, and one angle is equal to 90°.
So the triangle is isosceles and right-angled.

Exercise 2.8

The list below shows the various types of triangles.

A Equilateral
B Isosceles and acute-angled
C Isosceles and obtuse-angled
D Isosceles and right-angled
E Scalene and acute-angled
F Scalene and obtuse-angled
G Scalene and right-angled

Choose the correct label for each triangle below.

1 **2** **3**

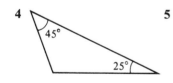

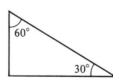

4 **5**

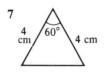

6 **7**

8 **9**

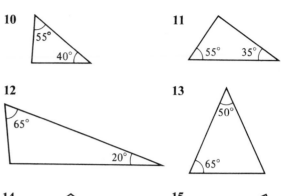

10 **11**

12 **13**

14 **15**

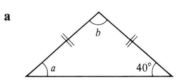

Example 8

Find the lettered angles in the following triangles.

a

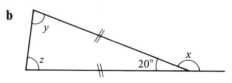

As the triangle is isosceles, $a = 40°$.
The sum of the angles in a triangle is 180°.

So $\hat{a} + 40° + \hat{b} = 180°$

$40° + 40° + \hat{b} = 180°$

$\therefore \qquad \hat{b} = 100°$

b

$\hat{x}$ and 20° are adjacent angles on a straight line.

So $\hat{x} + 20° = 180°$

$\hat{x} = 160°$

The triangle is isosceles

So $\hat{y} = \dfrac{180° - 20°}{2} = \dfrac{160°}{2} = 80°$

As $\hat{y} = \hat{z}$, then $z = 80°$.

14

Exercise 2.9

Find the lettered angles in each of the following.

1
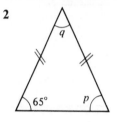

2

3
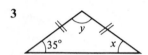

4
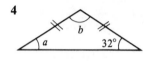

5
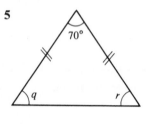

6
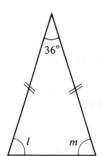

7

8

9
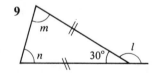

10

11
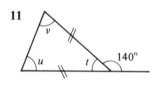

12

13
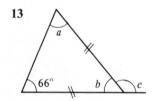

14
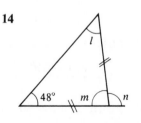

15
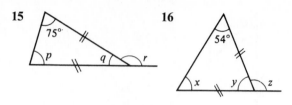

16

Sometimes the angle properties of straight lines, parallel lines, and triangles have to be used together in the same problem.

Example 9

Find $\hat{a}$, $\hat{b}$ and $\hat{c}$.

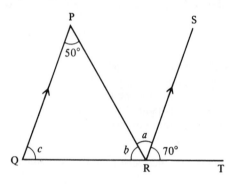

PQ is parallel to SR, so $\hat{a} = 50°$ because $\hat{a}$ and $50°$ are alternate angles.

QRT is a straight line

so $\hat{b} + \hat{a} + 70° = 180°$
$\hat{b} + 50° + 70° = 180°$
$\therefore \qquad \hat{b} = 60°$

PQR is a triangle
so $\hat{b} + 50° + \hat{c} = 180°$
$60° + 50° + \hat{c} = 180°$
$\therefore \qquad \hat{c} = 70°$

Exercise 2.10

Find the lettered angles in each of the following.

1
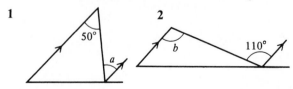

2

15

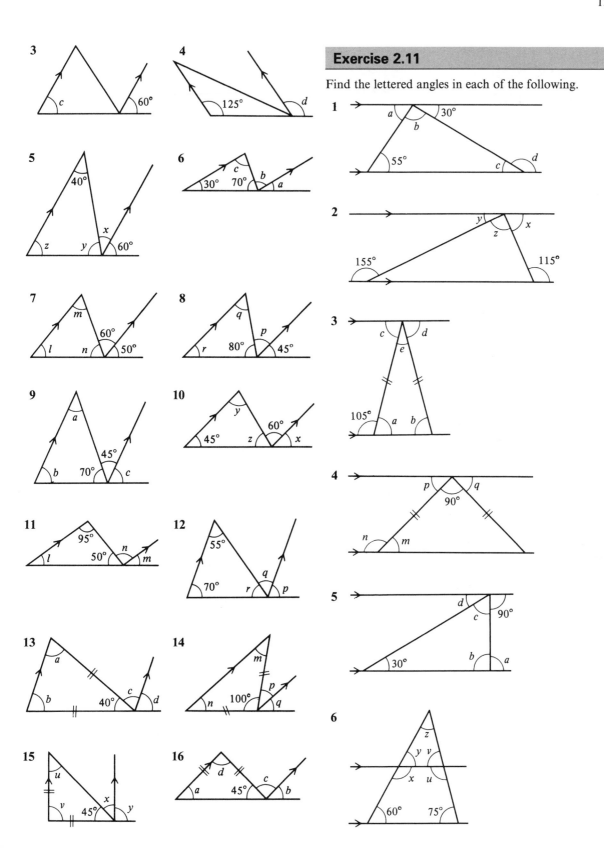

3

c   60°

4

125°   d

5

40°
z   y   x   60°

6

c   b
30°   70°   a

7

m
60°
l   n   50°

8

q
p
r   80°   45°

9

a
b   70°   45°   c

10

y
45°   z   60°   x

11

95°
l   50°   n   m

12

55°
70°   r   q   p

13

a
b   40°   c   d

14

m
n   100°   p   q

15

u
v   45°   x   y

16

d
a   45°   c   b

Exercise 2.11

Find the lettered angles in each of the following.

1

a   30°
b
55°   c   d

2

y
z   x
155°   115°

3

c   d
e
105°   a   b

4

p   q
90°
n   m

5

d
c   90°
30°   b   a

6

z
y   v
x   u
60°   75°

7

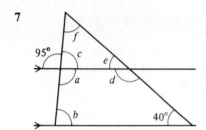

8

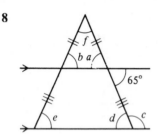

9

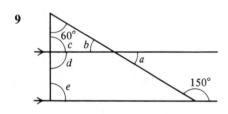

10

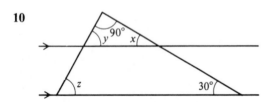

11

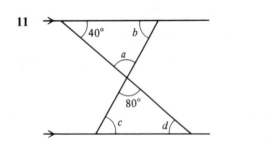

12

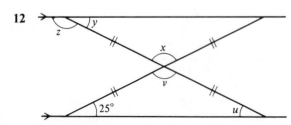

Quadrilaterals

A quadrilateral is a closed figure with four sides and four angles. The sum of these four angles is 360°.

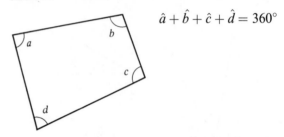

$$\hat{a} + \hat{b} + \hat{c} + \hat{d} = 360°$$

Exercise 2.12

Copy these special quadrilaterals carefully. You may find it easier to trace them.

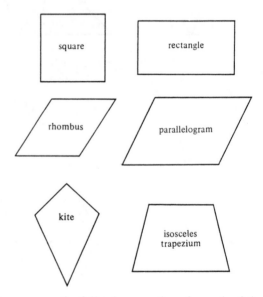

Then answer the following questions for each of the six shapes.

1 Are all the sides the same length?
2 Are the opposite sides equal?
3 Are the adjacent sides equal?
4 Are the opposite sides parallel?
5 Are all the angles right angles?
6 Are the opposite angles the same size?
7 Are the diagonals the same length?
8 Do the diagonals cut each other at right angles?
9 Is the shape symmetrical?
   If so, state
   a the number of lines of symmetry
   b the order of rotational symmetry (if any).

Exercise 2.13

Look at the diagrams in Exercise 2.12 and then copy and complete the following statements.

1 A *square* has...sides. It has...angles and each angle is...°. Each of its four sides are...and the opposite sides are...It has...lines of symmetry. The diagonals are...and bisect each other at ...angles.

2 A *rectangle* has...sides. It has...angles and each angle is...°. The opposite sides are...and...and it has...lines of symmetry.
The diagonals are...

3 A *rhombus* has...sides and...angles. All the sides are...and the opposite sides are...The... angles are equal and it has...lines of symmetry. The diagonals...each other at...angles.

4 A *parallelogram* has...sides and...angles. The opposite sides are...and...The...angles are equal. It has...lines of symmetry.

5 A *kite* has...sides and...angles. There are... pairs of...sides but the opposite sides are... equal. It has......of symmetry.
The diagonals cross and produce four...angles at this point.

6 An *isosceles trapezium* has...sides and...angles. One pair of opposite sides are...and one pair of opposite sides are...It has......of symmetry. The diagonals are...

Exercise 2.14

1 Look at the two right-angled triangles in the illustration.

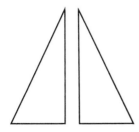

Draw a diagram to show how the pair can be arranged to form
a a rectangle
b a parallelogram
c a kite.

2 Look at the two isosceles triangles in the illustration.

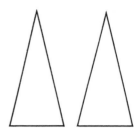

Draw a diagram to show how the pair can be arranged to form
a a parallelogram
b a rhombus
c a kite.

3 Look at the four right-angled triangles in the illustration.

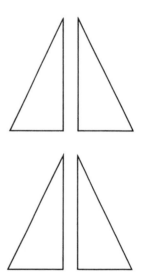

Draw a diagram to show how they can be arranged to form
a a rectangle
b a rhombus
c a parallelogram
d an isosceles trapezium.

4 Draw diagrams to show how
a two equilateral triangles can form a rhombus
b three equilateral triangles can form an isosceles trapezium
c four equilateral triangles can form a parallelogram
d four right-angled isosceles triangles can form a square.

Polygons

A *polygon* is a plane figure with three or more straight sides.

pentagon (five sides)   hexagon (six sides)   octagon (eight sides)

A *regular* polygon has all its sides equal in
length and all its angles equal in size.

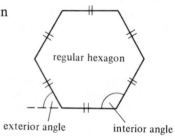

regular hexagon

exterior angle   interior angle

Example 10

Look at the diagram above of a regular hexagon and then answer the
following questions about it.

a How many equal interior angles are there?
b How many diagonals can be drawn from one vertex, and how many
triangles are so formed?
c What is the sum of the interior angles?
d What is the size of any one of these interior angles?

a There are 6 equal interior angles.
b Three diagonals can be drawn from one vertex; and 4 triangles are
formed.

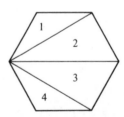

c The sum of the interior angles is the sum of the angles in the 4 triangles.
$$4 \times 180° = 720°$$
d Each of the interior angles is $720° \div 6 = 120°$

Exercise 2.15

Look at these regular polygons.

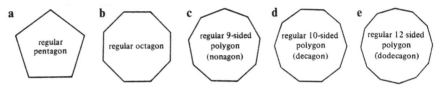

Then answer the following questions for all five shapes.

1 How many equal interior angles does the polygon have?
2 How many diagonals can be drawn from one vertex, and how many triangles are so formed?
3 What is the sum of the interior angles?
4 What is the size of any one of the interior angles?

Example 11

Look at the diagram opposite of a regular octagon.

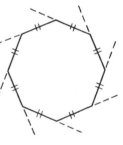

The octagon has rotational symmetry of order 8. This means that it will fit back into its original position 8 times as it is rotated through 360°.

Therefore its external angles must total 360°.

Answer the following questions.

a What is the size of one of the exterior angles?
b What is the sum of an exterior angle and an interior angle?

a The size of one exterior angle is 360° ÷ 8 = 45°
b Each pair of interior and exterior angles forms a straight line, so the sum of any pair is 180°.

In any polygon, the sum of the exterior angles is 360°.

Exercise 2.16

Look at these regular polygons.

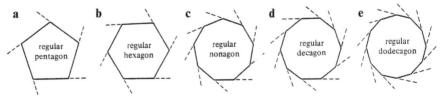

Then answer the following questions for all five shapes.

1 How many equal exterior angles does the polygon have?
2 What is the sum of the exterior angles?
3 What is the size of one of the equal exterior angles?
4 What is the sum of an exterior and an interior angle?

Example 12

a ABCDEF is a regular hexagon.
Describe the figures
(i) ABC   (ii) ACD   (iii) ADEF

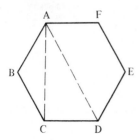

(i) ABC is an isosceles triangle.
(ii) ACD is a right-angled triangle.
(iii) ADEF is an isosceles trapezium.

b O is the centre of a regular hexagon
ABCDEF.
Describe the figures
(i) AOB   (ii) AOEF   (iii) BDEA

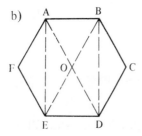

(i) AOB is an equilateral triangle.
(ii) AOEF is a rhombus.
(iii) BDEA is a rectangle.

Exercise 2.17

1 ABCDEF is a regular pentagon.
Describe the figures
(i) ABE   (ii) EBCD

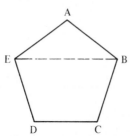

2 ABCDEF is a regular pentagon and O is its
centre.
If P, Q, R, S and T are the mid-points of the
sides, describe the figures
(i) DOC   (ii) AQOP   (iii) TOSD

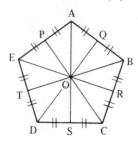

3 ABCDEFGH is a regular octagon.
Describe the figures
(i) ACEG   (ii) ACQP   (iii) ABCO
(iv) ABFG   (v) OQE   (vi) GOE
(vii) AGH

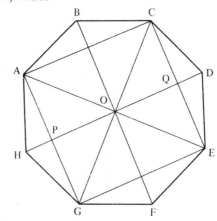

4 ABCDEFGHI is a regular nonagon.
Describe the figures
(i) ABI
(ii) BEFI
(iii) BCDE

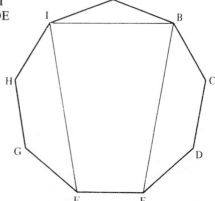

5 ABCDEFGHI is a regular nonagon.
  Describe the figures
   (i) KLMNPQRST
   (ii) IFC
   (iii) ABHI

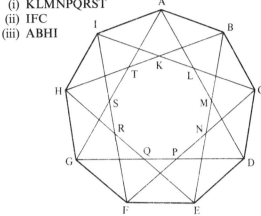

6 ABCDEFGHIJ is a regular decagon.
  Describe the figures
   (i) ACEGI
   (ii) KLMNP
   (iii) ACNI
   (iv) CEGI
   (v) AMNP

7 ABCDEFGHIJKL is a regular 12-sided polygon.
  Describe the figures
   (i) UVWXYZ
   (ii) PQS
   (iii) PWRZ
   (iv) UVSQ

8 ABCDEFGHIJKL is a regular 12-sided polygon.
  Describe the figures
   (i) WXYZ   (ii) MNPQRSTU

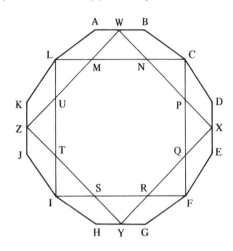

Congruence

Remember
Shapes that are alike in every possible way –
sides, angles and area – are said to be congruent.

Example 13

Draw sketches to show how four obtuse-angled
isosceles triangles, all of which are congruent,
can be arranged to make

a one large obtuse-angled isosceles triangle
b a parallelogram in two different ways.

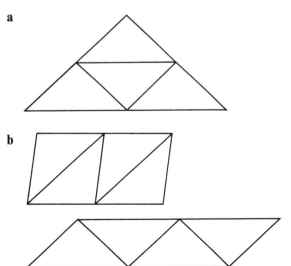

22

Exercise 2.18

1 Draw sketches to show how four acute-angled isosceles triangles, all of which are congruent, can be arranged to make
   a one large acute-angled isosceles triangle
   b a parallelogram in two different ways.

2 Draw a sketch to show how four congruent equilateral triangles can be arranged to make one large equilateral triangle.

3 Draw sketches to show how four right-angled isosceles triangles, all of which are congruent, can be arranged to make
   a one large right-angled isosceles triangle
   b a rectangle.

4 Draw sketches to show how four congruent right-angled triangles can be arranged to make
   a one large right-angled triangle
   b a rectangle in two different ways
   c a parallelogram in two different ways
   d an isosceles trapezium in two different ways.

5 Draw a sketch to show how six congruent equilateral triangles can be arranged to make a regular hexagon.

6 Draw a sketch to show how three congruent rhombuses can be arranged to make a hexagon.

7 The illustration shows four congruent right-angled triangles. The lengths of the sides which meet at the right angle are in the ratio of 2 : 1. Draw a sketch to show how the four triangles could be arranged to make a square.

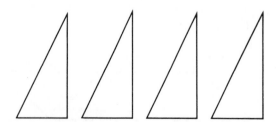

8 The illustration shows four right-angled isosceles triangles, all of which are congruent, and one square whose dimension is equal to the length of the longest side of any of the triangles.
Draw a sketch to show how the five figures could be arranged to make a square.

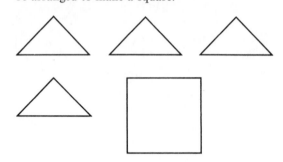

9 The illustration shows four congruent isosceles trapeziums and one square. The lengths of the parallel sides of the trapeziums are in the ratio of 3 : 1, and the dimension of the square is equal to the length of the shorter parallel side of any of the trapeziums.
Draw a sketch to show how the five figures could be arranged to make a square.

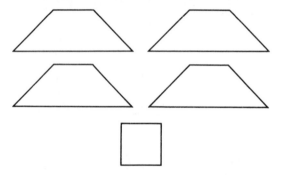

10 The illustration shows a kite whose longer pair of equal sides meet at an angle of 90°, and whose illustrated diagonal is equal in length to these two sides. Draw a sketch to show how four congruent kites of this kind could be arranged to make a regular octagon.

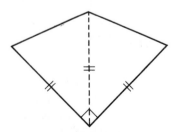

Example 14

Pick out and name the three pairs of congruent triangles from the kite ABCD.

The congruent triangles are

a ADM and ABM
b ADC and ABC
c DMC and BMC

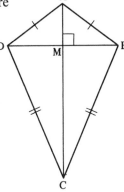

Exercise 2.19

1 Pick out and name the single pair of congruent triangles from the isosceles trapezium ABCD.

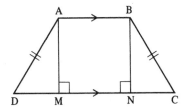

2 Pick out and name the single pair of congruent triangles from the isosceles triangle ABC.

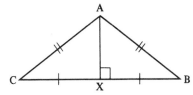

3 Pick out and name the single pair of congruent triangles from the kite ABCD.

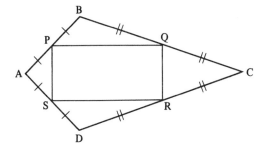

4 Pick out and name the two pairs of congruent triangles from the regular hexagon ABCDEF.

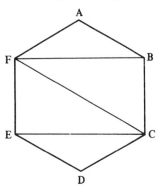

5 Pick out and name the two pairs of congruent triangles from the rhombus ABCD. (W, X, Y and Z are the mid-points of the sides.)

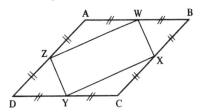

6 Pick out and name the two pairs of congruent triangles from the isosceles trapezium ABCD. (K, L, M and N are the mid-points of the sides.)

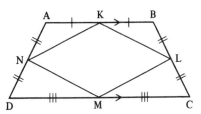

7 Pick out and name the two pairs of congruent triangles from the regular pentagon ABCDE. (M is the mid-point of CD.)

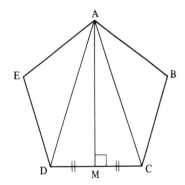

24

8 Pick out and name the three pairs of congruent triangles from the kite ABCD.

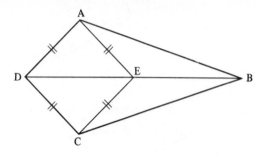

9 Pick out and name the three pairs of congruent triangles from the regular octagon ABCDEFGH.

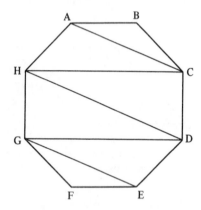

10 Pick out and name the three pairs of congruent triangles from the isosceles trapezium ABCD.

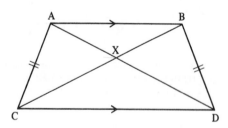

1 Look at the star pattern illustrated.
  a Name the polygon ABCDEF.
  b Find the sizes of the following angles
    (i) FÂB   (ii) PÂB
    (iii) the vertex angle AP̂B.

c What is the sum of all the vertex angles in the pattern?

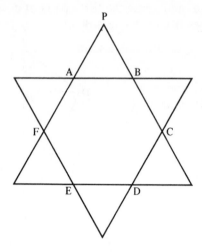

2 Look at the star pattern illustrated.

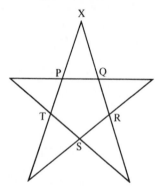

  a Name the polygon PQRST.
  b Find the sizes of the following angles
    (i) TP̂Q   (ii) XP̂Q
    (iii) the vertex angle PX̂Q.
  c What is the sum of all the vertex angles in the pattern?

3 The diagram illustrates the top of a fence stake. Find the size of angles *a* and *b*.

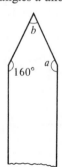

4 The head of the arrow is an isosceles triangle and its two flights are parallelograms.

Find the size of the angles *a*, *b* and *c*.

5 The equilateral triangle illustrated is made from four smaller triangles of the same kind which are all congruent.

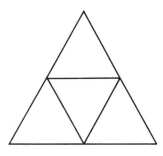

Draw a sketch which shows how the four triangles could be rearranged to make a parallelogram.

6 The rectangle illustrated is made from one isosceles triangle and two right-angled triangles which are congruent.

Draw sketches to show how the same three figures could be rearranged to make
 (i) an isosceles trapezium
 (ii) a parallelogram
 (iii) a rhombus.

7 The square illustrated is made from a smaller square and four isosceles right-angled triangles which are congruent.

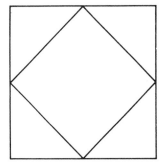

Draw sketches to show how the same five figures could be rearranged to make
 (i) an isosceles trapezium
 (ii) a parallelogram
 (iii) one large isosceles right-angled triangle
 (iv) a rectangle.

Unit 3 Sequences

A *sequence* is a set of numbers such that each number is related to the next by a *rule*. The numbers are called the *terms* of the sequence.

Example 1

Give the rule and next two terms of each sequence

a 2, 4, 6, 8, . . .   **b** 3, 9, 27, 81, . . .
c 1, 4, 10, 22, . . .

a The rule is that each term is 2 more than the one before it.
   The next two terms are 10 and 12.
b The rule is that each term is 3 times the one before it.
   The next two terms are 243 and 729.
c The rule is that each term is 2 times the one before it, plus 2.
   The next two terms are 46 and 94.

Exercise 3.1

Give the rule and next two terms of each sequence.

1 1, 3, 5, 7, . . .
2 1, 2, 4, 8, . . .
3 1.2, 1.4, 1.6, 1.8, . . .
4 1, 4, 16, 64, . . .
5 7, 20, 33, 46, . . .
6 1, 1, 2, 3, 5, 8, . . .
7 1, 2, 4, 8, 32, . . .
8 1, 5, 25, 125, . . .
9 0.1, 0.5, 2.5, 12.5, . . .
10 200, 150, 100, 50, . . .
11 1000, 500, 250, 125, . . .
12 100, 50, 25, 12.5, . . .
13 1000, 700, 400, 100, . . .
14 32, 8, 2, 0.5, . . .
15 1, 10, 100, 1000, . . .
16 21, 32, 43, 54, . . .
17 1, 3, 7, 15, . . .
18 1, 4, 13, 40, . . .
19 1, 2, 5, 14, . . .
20 1, 2, 7, 32, . . .

Example 2

The first term of a sequence is 1 and the rule for the sequence is that each term is 3 times the one before it, plus 1.
Write down the first 5 terms of the sequence.

Starting with 1 and applying the rule we have

   1, 4, 13, 40, 121, . . .

Exercise 3.2

Write down the first five terms of each of the following sequences.

1 The first term is 1 and the rule for the sequence is that each term is 3 times the one before it.
2 The first term is 6 and the rule for the sequence is that each term is the one before it plus 5.
3 The first term is 2 and the rule for the sequence is that each term is 3 times the one before it.
4 The first term is 100 and the rule for the sequence is that each term is the one before it minus 5.
5 The first term is 4000 and the rule for the sequence is that each term is the one before it, divided by 4.
6 The first term is 1 and the rule for the sequence is that each term is 2 times the one before it, plus 5.
7 The first term is 4 and the rule for the sequence is that each term is 2 times the one before it, minus 1.
8 The first term is 1 and the rule for the sequence is that each term is 4 times the one before it, plus 3.
9 The first term is 1000 and the rule for the sequence is that each term is the one before it, divided by 5, plus 10.
10 The first term is 1 and the rule for the sequence is that each term is 10 times the one before it, plus 10.

The sequence 1, 2, 3, 4, 5, 6, 7, 8, . . . is the most simple of all. This sequence is called the *natural number* sequence.

The terms of other sequences can often be formed from the sequence of natural numbers.

Example 3

a Describe how the sequence of even numbers is produced from the sequence of natural numbers.
b Describe how the sequence of odd numbers is produced from the sequence of natural numbers.

a Compare the two sequences.

$$
\begin{array}{cccccc}
1 & 2 & 3 & 4 & 5 & 6 \\
\downarrow & \downarrow & \downarrow & \downarrow & \downarrow & \downarrow \\
2 & 4 & 6 & 8 & 10 & 12
\end{array}
$$

We see that the even numbers are produced by multiplying the natural numbers by 2.

b Compare the two sequences

$$
\begin{array}{cccccc}
1 & 2 & 3 & 4 & 5 & 6 \\
\downarrow & \downarrow & \downarrow & \downarrow & \downarrow & \downarrow \\
1 & 3 & 5 & 7 & 9 & 11
\end{array}
$$

We see that the odd numbers are produced by multiplying the natural numbers by 2 and then subtracting 1.

Exercise 3.3

Describe how each sequence is produced from the sequence of natural numbers and give the next two terms.

1 3, 6, 9, 12, ...
2 2, 5, 8, 11, ...
3 −5, −4, −3, −2, ...
4 4, 8, 12, 16, ...
5 5, 9, 13, 17, ...
6 6, 10, 14, 18, ...
7 3, 7, 11, 15, ...
8 2, 6, 10, 14, ...
9 5, 10, 15, 20, ...
10 6, 11, 16, 21, ...
11 7, 12, 17, 22, ...
12 8, 13, 18, 23, ...
13 4, 9, 14, 19, ...
14 0, 5, 10, 15, ...
15 −1, 4, 9, 14, ...
16 5, 11, 17, 23, ...
17 7, 13, 19, 25, ...
18 13, 23, 33, 43, ...
19 7, 17, 27, 37, ...
20 0.1, 0.2, 0.3, 0.4, ...

Example 4

Write down the first 5 terms and the 10th term of the sequence produced by multiplying the natural numbers by 8 and subtracting 5.

Applying these operations to the natural numbers we have

$$
\begin{array}{cccccc}
1 & 2 & 3 & 4 & 5 & 10 \\
\downarrow & \downarrow & \downarrow & \downarrow & \downarrow & \downarrow \\
3 & 11 & 19 & 27 & 35 & 75
\end{array}
$$

Exercise 3.4

Write down the first 5 terms and the 10th term of the sequence produced by changing the sequence of natural numbers in the following ways

1 multiplying by 7
2 adding 11
3 subtracting 5
4 dividing by 2
5 multiplying by 2 and adding 11
6 adding 11 and multiplying by 2
7 multiplying by 7 and subtracting 1
8 subtracting 1 and multiplying by 7
9 dividing by 2 and adding 5
10 adding 5 and dividing by 2
11 dividing by 4 and subtracting 4
12 subtracting 4 and dividing by 4
13 multiplying by 5 and adding 2
14 adding 2 and multiplying by 5
15 multiplying by 3 and adding 12
16 adding 12 and multiplying by 3
17 multiplying by 1.5 and adding 0.5
18 adding 0.5 and multiplying by 1.5
19 multiplying by 0.5 and subtracting 1.5
20 subtracting 1.5 and multiplying by 0.5

We can use mathematical shorthand to describe sequences.

We use a capital letter of the alphabet, followed by a suffix to represent each term.

For example, if the capital letter T is used to represent the terms of the sequence, 2, 4, 6, 8, ...
Then

$$
\begin{aligned}
T_1 &= 2 \\
T_2 &= 4 \\
T_3 &= 6 \\
T_4 &= 8
\end{aligned}
$$

A general term of the sequence is represented by T_n, where n can be any whole number. The term after T_n will be T_{n+1}, the term after that T_{n+2} and so on.

The rule for the sequence can also be written in mathematical shorthand. For this sequence the rule is

$$
T_{n+1} = T_n + 2
$$

This means, to find the term after T_n, add 2 to T_n.

28

Example 5

Write the rule for each sequence using mathematical shorthand.

a 1, 5, 9, 13,...
   Each term is formed by adding 4 to the one before it, so the rule is $T_{n+1} = T_n + 4$

b 1, 5, 25, 125,...
   Each term is formed by multiplying the one before it by 5, so the rule is $T_{n+1} = 5T_n$

c 1, 3, 7, 15,...
   Each term is formed by multiplying the one before it by 2, and then adding 1, so the rule is $T_{n+1} = 2T_n + 1$

Exercise 3.5

Write the rule for each sequence using mathematical shorthand.

1 1, 8, 15, 22,...   **2** 2, 4, 8, 16,...
3 3, 7, 11, 15,...   **4** 5, 15, 45, 135,...
5 17, 19, 21, 23,...   **6** 1, 7, 49, 343,...
7 12, 10, 8, 6,...   **8** 100, 50, 25, 12.5,...
9 200, 190, 180, 170,...   **10** 1000, 100, 10, 1,...
11 1, 2, 4, 8,...   **12** 1, 3, 7, 15,...
13 1, 5, 13, 29,...   **14** 1, 6, 16, 36,...
15 1, 3, 9, 27,...   **16** 1, 4, 13, 40,...
17 1, 5, 17, 53,...   **18** 1, 2, 5, 14,...
19 1, 4, 16, 64,...   **20** 1, 2, 6, 22,...

Example 6

Write the first 5 terms of the sequence for which $T_1 = 1$ and $T_{n+1} = 2T_n + 5$

Starting with 1 and applying the rule we have

$$1, 7, 19, 43, 91,...$$

Exercise 3.6

Write down the first five terms of each of the following sequences.

1 $T_1 = 1$ $T_{n+1} = T_n + 13$
2 $T_1 = 1$ $T_{n+1} = T_n + 4$
3 $T_1 = 1$ $T_{n+1} = 6T_n$
4 $T_1 = 1$ $T_{n+1} = 8T_n$
5 $T_1 = 20$ $T_{n+1} = T_n - 5$
6 $T_1 = 12$ $T_{n+1} = T_n - 1$
7 $T_1 = 1000$ $T_{n+1} = T_n \div 10$
8 $T_1 = 512$ $T_{n+1} = T_n \div 2$
9 $T_1 = 1$ $T_{n+1} = 2T_n + 6$

10 $T_1 = 1$ $T_{n+1} = 6T_n + 2$
11 $T_1 = 1$ $T_{n+1} = 5T_n - 3$
12 $T_1 = 1$ $T_{n+1} = 7T_n - 1$
13 $T_1 = 260$ $T_{n+1} = (T_n \div 2) + 2$
14 $T_1 = 11\,725$ $T_{n+1} = (T_n \div 5) + 5$
15 $T_1 = 603$ $T_{n+1} = (T_n \div 3) - 3$
16 $T_1 = 1956$ $T_{n+1} = (T_n \div 4) - 5$
17 $T_1 = 1$ $T_{n+1} = 3T_n + 13$
18 $T_1 = 1$ $T_{n+1} = 7T_n + 1$
19 $T_1 = 1$ $T_{n+1} = 10T_n + 10$
20 $T_1 = 1$ $T_{n+1} = 100T_n - 99$

Example 7

Describe, using mathematical shorthand, how the sequence of odd numbers is produced from the sequence of natural numbers.

Numbering the terms using the sequence of natural numbers

T_1	T_2	T_3	T_4	T_5
↓	↓	↓	↓	↓
1	3	5	7	9

We can write $T_n = 2n - 1$, meaning that each term is formed by multiplying the term number by 2, then subtracting 1.

When we write $T_n = 2n - 1$, we have *written a formula for the nth term of the sequence.*

Example 8

Write a formula for the *n*th term of the sequence

$$6, 10, 14, 18,...$$

Numbering the terms using the sequence of natural numbers

T_1	T_2	T_3	T_4
↓	↓	↓	↓
6	10	14	18

We can see the sequence starts with 6 and each term is formed by adding 4.

$$T_1 = 6$$
$$T_2 = 6 + 4$$
$$T_3 = 6 + 4 \times 2$$
$$T_4 = 6 + 4 \times 3$$
$$T_n = 6 + 4 \times (n - 1)$$
$$T_n = 6 + 4n - 4 = 4n + 2$$

Exercise 3.7

Write a formula for the nth term of the following sequences.

1. $3, 6, 9, 12, \ldots$
2. $4, 8, 12, 16, \ldots$
3. $5, 10, 15, 20, \ldots$
4. $6, 12, 18, 24, \ldots$
5. $9, 18, 27, 36, \ldots$
6. $9, 10, 11, 12, \ldots$
7. $7, 8, 9, 10, \ldots$
8. $101, 102, 103, 104, 105, \ldots$
9. $-5, -4, -3, -2, \ldots$
10. $-10, -9, -8, -7, \ldots$
11. $0.5, 1, 1.5, 2, \ldots$
12. $0.25, 0.5, 0.75, 1.0, \ldots$
13. $0.01, 0.02, 0.03, 0.04, \ldots$
14. $0.125, 0.25, 0.325, 0.5, \ldots$
15. $0.2, 0.4, 0.6, 0.8, \ldots$
16. $3, 5, 7, 9, \ldots$
17. $6, 9, 12, 15, \ldots$
18. $11, 21, 31, 41, \ldots$
19. $20, 30, 40, 50, \ldots$
20. $4, 6, 8, 10, \ldots$

We can use a formula for the nth term of a sequence to produce any term we want.

Example 9

Write down the first 5 terms and the 10th term of the sequence produced by the formula $T_n = 7n + 10$

Applying this formula to the natural numbers we have

T_1	T_2	T_3	T_4	T_5	T_{10}
↓	↓	↓	↓	↓	↓
17	24	31	38	45	80

Exercise 3.8

Write down the first 5 terms and the 10th term of the sequences produced by the following formulae.

1. $T_n = 5n + 4$
2. $T_n = 5n - 4$
3. $T_n = 4n + 5$
4. $T_n = 4n - 5$
5. $T_n = 5n \div 4$
6. $T_n = 4n \div 5$
7. $T_n = (n \div 4) + 5$
8. $T_n = (n \div 5) + 4$
9. $T_n = (n \div 4) - 5$
10. $T_n = (n \div 5) - 4$
11. $T_n = (n + 4) \div 5$
12. $T_n = (n + 5) \div 4$
13. $T_n = (n - 4) \div 5$
14. $T_n = (n - 5) \div 4$
15. $T_n = 5(n - 4)$
16. $T_n = 4(n - 5)$

Some sequences are produced by multiplying each term by a fixed number.
Sequences like these always have a formula which involves a power of the multiplying number.

Example 10

Write a formula for the nth term of the sequence

$$3, 6, 12, 24, \ldots$$

Numbering the terms using the sequence of natural numbers

T_1	T_2	T_3	T_4
↓	↓	↓	↓
3	6	12	24

We can see that the sequence starts with 3 and each new term is formed by multiplying the term before by 2.

$$T_1 = 3$$
$$T_2 = 3 \times 2$$
$$T_3 = 3 \times 2 \times 2 = 3 \times 2^2$$
$$T_4 = 3 \times 2 \times 2 \times 2 = 3 \times 2^3$$

The nth term will be 3 multiplied by 2 a total of $(n - 1)$ times.
This can be written

$$T_n = 3 \times 2^{(n-1)}$$

If we check and apply this formula to the first and second terms of the sequence it becomes

$$T_1 = 3 \times 2^{(1-1)} = 3 \times 2^0$$

Any number to the power zero is equal to 1, so

$$T_1 = 3 \times 1 = 3, \text{ which is correct.}$$
$$T_2 = 3 \times 2^{(2-1)} = 3 \times 2^1$$

Any number to the power one is equal to itself, so

$$T_2 = 3 \times 2 = 6, \text{ which is correct.}$$

Exercise 3.9

Write a formula for the nth term of the following sequences.

1 5, 10, 20, 40, ...
2 6, 12, 24, 48, ...
3 7, 14, 28, 56, ...
4 10, 20, 40, 80, ...
5 8, 16, 32, 64, ...
6 2, 4, 8, 16, ...
7 2, 6, 18, 54, ...
8 1, 3, 9, 27, ...
9 1, 2, 4, 8, ...
10 1, 10, 100, 1000, ...
11 2, 10, 50, 250, ...
12 7, 77, 847, 9317, ...
13 4, 16, 64, 256, ...
14 1, 9, 81, 729, ...
15 3, 27, 243, 2187, ...
16 1, 6, 36, 216, ...
17 1, 8, 64, 512, ...
18 5, 40, 320, 2560, ...
19 2, 16, 128, 1024, ...
20 3, 9, 27, 81, ...

Example 11

Write down the first 4 terms and the 10th term of the sequence produced by the formula

$$T_n = 6 \times 5^{(n-1)}$$

Applying this formula to the natural numbers we have

$$T_1 = 6 \times 5^{(1-1)} = 6 \times 5^0 = 6 \times 1 = 6$$
$$T_2 = 6 \times 5^{(2-1)} = 6 \times 5^1 = 6 \times 5 = 30$$
$$T_3 = 6 \times 5^{(3-1)} = 6 \times 5^2 = 6 \times 25 = 150$$
$$T_4 = 6 \times 5^{(4-1)} = 6 \times 5^3 = 6 \times 125 = 750$$

The tenth term

$$T_{10} = 6 \times 5^{(10-1)} = 6 \times 5^9 = 6 \times 1\,953\,125$$
$$= 11\,718\,750$$

Exercise 3.10

Write down the first 4 terms and the 10th term of the sequences produced by the following formulae.

1 $T_n = 5 \times 6^{(n-1)}$
2 $T_n = 4 \times 7^{(n-1)}$
3 $T_n = 7 \times 4^{(n-1)}$
4 $T_n = 8 \times 3^{(n-1)}$
5 $T_n = 3 \times 8^{(n-1)}$
6 $T_n = 2 \times 7^{(n-1)}$
7 $T_n = 7 \times 2^{(n-1)}$
8 $T_n = 4^{(n-1)}$
9 $T_n = 4^n$
10 $T_n = 3 \times 10^{(n-1)}$
11 $T_n = 10 \times 3^{(n-1)}$
12 $T_n = 3^{(n-1)}$
13 $T_n = 10^n$
14 $T_n = 5 \times 3^n$
15 $T_n = 3 \times 5^n$
16 $T_n = 3 \times 5^{(n-1)}$

Example 12

A gardener plants borders with roses and marigolds using the following pattern.

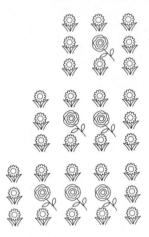

Find a formula for the number of marigolds that will be planted with n roses.
How many marigolds will be planted with 10 roses?

The number of roses is the sequence of natural numbers.
Arranging the number of marigolds as the terms of a sequence we have

$$\begin{array}{ccc} T_1 & T_2 & T_3 \\ \downarrow & \downarrow & \downarrow \\ 8 & 10 & 12 \end{array}$$

We can see the sequence starts with 8 and each term is formed by adding 2.

$$T_1 = 8$$

$$T_2 = 8 + 2$$

$$T_3 = 8 + 2 \times 2$$

$$T_n = 8 + 2 \times (n - 1)$$

$$T_n = 8 + 2n - 2$$

$$T_n = 2n + 6$$

Using this formula with $n = 10$, we find that 26 marigolds will be planted with 10 roses.

Exercise 3.11

1 A gardener plants borders with roses and marigolds using the following patterns.
In each case, find a formula for the number of marigolds that will be planted with n roses.
How many marigolds will be planted with 10 roses?

a

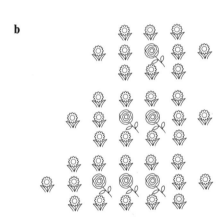

b

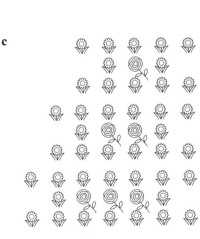

c

2 Jo has £20 in her piggy bank.
In each case, find a formula for the amount of money she will have in the piggy bank after n weeks if she saves
a £3 a week   b £1 a week
c £2 a week   d £5 a week
e £10 a week

3 Caroline has won a prize of 1000 tins of dog food.

In each case, find a formula for the number of tins she will have left after n weeks if her dog eats
a 5 tins a week   b 3 tins a week
c 7 tins a week   d 10 tins a week
e 14 tins a week

4 An author has signed a contract to write a book of 400 pages.
In each case, find a formula for the number of pages left to write after n days if the author writes
a 10 pages a day   b 20 pages a day
c 5 pages a day   d 17 pages a day
e 25 pages a day

5 William is playing Salima at cards, gambling 10 p per game. Salima wins the first game and William suggests they double the bet to 20 p (he hopes to win and get all his money back). Salima wins the second game as well and William suggests they double the bet to 40 p, ...

a Salima keeps winning! She wins the 1st game, the 2nd game, the 3rd game and so on.
Find a formula for the bet William will have to make to win all his money back in their nth game if Salima keeps winning!
b What would be the bet in the 10th game?

6 A very old story tells of a prince who saved a king's life. The king told the prince he could name his own reward, up to half his kingdom.
The prince pointed to the 64 squares on a chess board and said, 'I will have that board filled with rice. I want you to put 1 grain on the first square, 2 grains on the second square, 4 grains on the third square, 8 grains on the fourth square and so on, until the board is full. If you cannot fulfil this request then give me the whole kingdom.' The king quickly agreed, because everyone thought the prince had made a very unwise choice for his reward, which would only amount to a bucket or two of rice.

a Find a formula for the number of grains on the *n*th square of the board.
b How many grains of rice would be needed for the 20th square?
c How many grains of rice would be needed for the 64th square?
d What do you think the prince's reward actually was?

7 The population of Gastropoll is currently 25 000 but it is increasing each year. The planning department of the town council have discovered that at the end of each year the population is 1.1 times greater than at the start of the year.
a Find a formula for the population of Gastropoll after *n* years.
b How many years will it be before the population is greater than 36 000?
c The population of Strovney is currently 20 000 but is 1.2 times greater at the end of each year. How many years will it take before Strovney has a greater population than Gastropoll?

8 Jade breeds rabbits. Currently she owns 24 but she finds that this number trebles every year.

a Find a formula for the number of rabbits Jade will own in *n* years time.
b How many rabbits did Jade own a year ago?
c If this progress continues, how many rabbits will she own in 10 years?
d How long do you think Jade will be able to continue this breeding sequence?

The sequence of square numbers is

$$T_1 \quad T_2 \quad T_3 \quad T_4 \quad T_5, \ldots$$
$$\downarrow \quad \downarrow \quad \downarrow \quad \downarrow \quad \downarrow$$
$$1 \quad 4 \quad 9 \quad 16 \quad 25, \ldots$$

We can see that the formula for the *n*th term of this sequence is

$$T_n = n^2$$

Example 13

Write down the first 5 terms of the sequence produced by the formula $T_n = n^2 + n$

Applying the formula we have

$$T_1 = 1 \times 1 + 1 = 2$$
$$T_2 = 2 \times 2 + 2 = 6$$
$$T_3 = 3 \times 3 + 3 = 12$$
$$T_4 = 4 \times 4 + 4 = 20$$
$$T_5 = 5 \times 5 + 5 = 30$$

Exercise 3.12

Write down the first 5 terms of the sequences produced by the following formulae.

1 $T_n = 2n^2$ **2** $T_n = 3n^2$

3 $T_n = 5n^2$
4 $T_n = n^2 + 1$
5 $T_n = n^2 - 1$
6 $T_n = n^2 + 2$
7 $T_n = n^2 - 2$
8 $T_n = n^2 - n$
9 $T_n = 2n^2 + 1$
10 $T_n = 2n^2 + n$
11 $T_n = n^2 + n + 1$
12 $T_n = n^2 + n + 5$
13 $T_n = 2n^2 + n + 2$
14 $T_n = 2n^2 + 2n + 2$
15 $T_n = 2n^2 - n$
16 $T_n = 2n^2 - 2n$
17 $T_n = 2n^2 - n + 5$
18 $T_n = n^2 - 2n + 5$
19 $T_n = n^2 - 3n + 1$
20 $T_n = 3n^2 - n + 3$

Exercise 3.13

1 The triangular numbers are

T_1	T_2	T_3	T_4	$T_5,\ldots$
↓	↓	↓	↓	↓
1	3	6	10	15,...

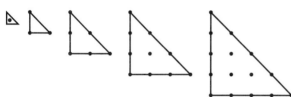

If two identical triangular numbers are placed together they form a rectangle.

2×1 2×3

a Draw the rectangles formed by the next 5 triangular numbers.
b How big would the rectangle formed from the 12th triangular number be?
c How big would the rectangle formed from the 100th triangular number be?
d How big would the rectangle formed from the nth triangular number be?
e Write down a formula for the nth triangular number.

2 When groups of French people meet, usually everyone shakes hands with everyone else. Three French friends meet. Each person shakes hands with the other two.
a How many handshakes will there be in total?
b How many handshakes will there be in total if 4 friends meet?

c How many handshakes will there be in total if 5 friends meet?
d How many handshakes will there be in total if n friends meet?

3 There are 22 teams in the Football Premier League. Each team plays all the other teams both 'at home' and 'away'.
a How many games are played each season?
b How many games would be played in a league with n teams?

4 A 3 cm cube of wood is painted red and then cut into individual 1 cm cubes.

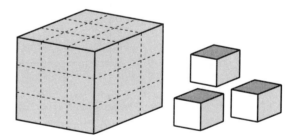

a How many of the 1 cm cubes will be painted on no faces?
b How many of the 1 cm cubes will be painted on one face?
c How many of the 1 cm cubes will be painted on two faces?
d How many of the 1 cm cubes will be painted on three faces?
e How many of each type of 1 cm cube would there be if you cut up a 5 cm cube?
f Find formulae for the number of each type of 1 cm cube if you cut up an n cm cube.

Unit 4 Area

Reminder

The area of a rectangle is
  length × width

The area of a triangle is
  $$\frac{\text{base} \times \text{height}}{2}$$

The perimeter of a shape is the distance all the way around the shape.

Exercise 4.1

For questions **1** to **13** find
a the area
b the perimeter of each shape where possible.

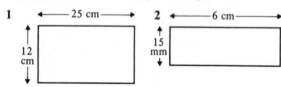

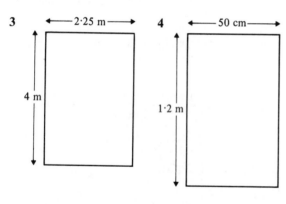

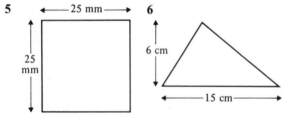

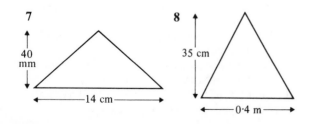

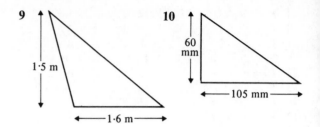

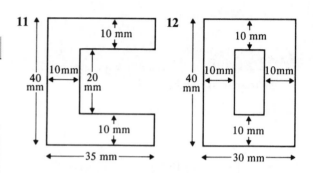

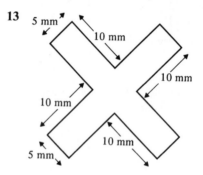

14 The diagram shows the dimensions of the floor of a room. Find
a the area of the room
b the cost of covering it with a fitted carpet if the carpet is sold at £5.70 per square metre.

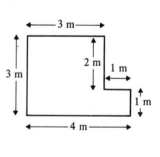

15 A room is 5 m long, 4 m wide and 2.5 m high. Find
a the total surface area of the four walls
b the volume of paint required to decorate the walls if each square metre requires 0.1 litres.

16 The diagram shows a square border path around a small garden plot. Find the area of each of the paving stones.

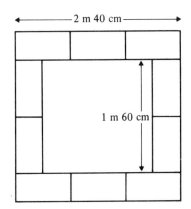

Example 1

Find the area of the kite ABCD.

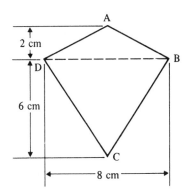

The line BD splits the kite into two triangles, ABD and BCD.

area of ABD $= \frac{1}{2}$ (base $\times$ height)

$= \frac{1}{2} (8 \times 2) = 8 \, \text{cm}^2$

area of BCD $= \frac{1}{2}$ (base $\times$ height)

$= \frac{1}{2} (8 \times 6) = 24 \, \text{cm}^2$

$\therefore$ area of kite $= 8 \, \text{cm}^2 + 24 \, \text{cm}^2$

$= 32 \, \text{cm}^2$

Example 2

Find the area of the trapezium PQRS.

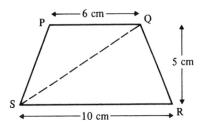

The line QS splits the trapezium into two triangles, PQS and QRS.

area of PQS $= \frac{1}{2}$ (base $\times$ height)

$= \frac{1}{2} (6 \times 5) = 15 \, \text{cm}^2$

area of QRS $= \frac{1}{2}$ (base $\times$ height)

$= \frac{1}{2} (10 \times 5) = 25 \, \text{cm}^2$

$\therefore$ area of trapezium $= 15 \, \text{cm}^2 + 25 \, \text{cm}^2$

$= 40 \, \text{cm}^2$

Exercise 4.2

Find the area of the following shapes.

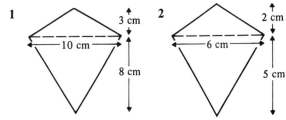

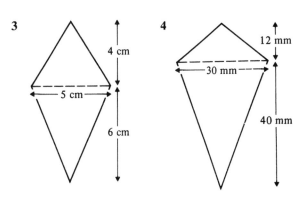

36

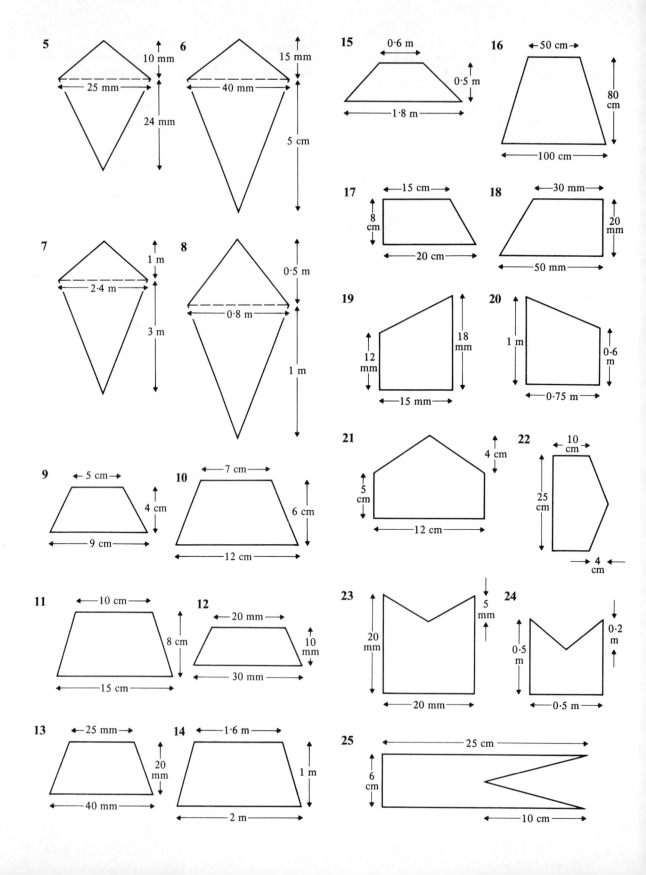

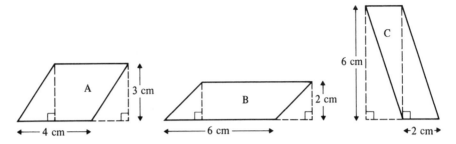

The area of each of the above parallelograms is $12\,\text{cm}^2$ as

area of parallelogram = base × perpendicular height

so the area of A $= 4 \times 3 = 12\,\text{cm}^2$
the area of B $= 6 \times 2 = 12\,\text{cm}^2$
the area of C $= 2 \times 6 = 12\,\text{cm}^2$

Example 3

Find the area of the following parallelograms:

a 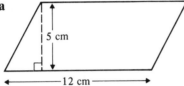 b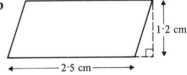

a area = base × height
$= 12 \times 5$
$= 60\,\text{cm}^2$

b area = base × height
$= 2.5 \times 1.2$
$= 3.00$ or $3\,\text{cm}^2$

Exercise 4.3

Find the area of the following parallelograms.

1 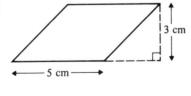 2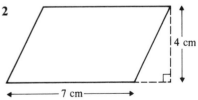

3 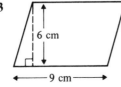 4 5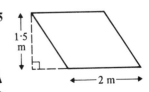

Find the area of the following parallelograms from the details given.

	base	height		base	height		base	height
6	12 cm	4 cm	11	40 mm	25 mm	16	7.5 m	4 m
7	15 cm	8 cm	12	2.4 m	4 m	17	4 m	3.5 m
8	25 cm	12 cm	13	5 m	1.5 m	18	2.5 m	2.4 m
9	30 mm	20 mm	14	3 cm	1.8 cm	19	3.2 m	2.5 m
10	50 mm	40 mm	15	6 cm	4.5 cm	20	1.5 cm	1.2 cm

Example 4

a Parallelogram ABCD has an area of 30 cm².
If the perpendicular height is 5 cm, find the length of the base DC.

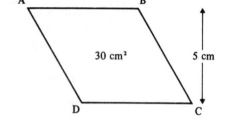

a area = base × height
so 30 = DC × 5
therefore DC = 30 ÷ 5
= 6 cm

b Parallelogram ABCD has an area of 10 mm².
If the base DC is 4 mm in length, find the perpendicular height.

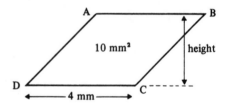

b area = base × height
so 10 = 4 × height
therefore height = $10 \div 4 = 2\frac{1}{2}$ mm

Exercise 4.4

Copy and complete the following table of dimensions of parallelograms.

	base	height	area
1		4 cm	24 cm²
2		5 cm	40 cm²
3		3 cm	21 cm²
4	12 cm		36 cm²
5	20 cm		180 cm²
6	15 cm		90 cm²
7		30 mm	1200 mm²
8		50 mm	3000 mm²
9		20 mm	500 mm²
10	80 mm		3600 mm²
11	60 mm		2100 mm²

	base	height	area
12		1.5 cm	6 cm²
13		2.5 cm	7.5 cm²
14	1.8 cm		7.2 cm²
15	1.6 cm		9.6 cm²
16	3.5 m		10.5 m²
17	2.4 m		12 m²
18		7.5 m	60 m²
19		1.6 m	4 m²
20		3.2 m	4.8 m²

The areas of some shapes may be found more easily by subtraction.

Example 5

A rectangular lawn measures 8 m by 5 m. It is surrounded by a path of width $\frac{1}{2}$ m.
Find the area of the path, shown shaded.

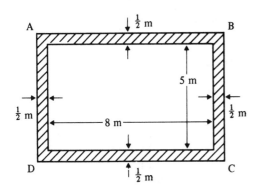

$AB = \frac{1}{2}\,m + 8\,m + \frac{1}{2}\,m = 9\,m$

$BC = \frac{1}{2}\,m + 5\,m + \frac{1}{2}\,m = 6\,m$

So   area $ABCD = 9\,m \times 6\,m = 54\,m^2$

    area of lawn $= 8\,m \times 5\,m = 40\,m^2$

$\therefore$ area of path $= 54\,m^2 - 40\,m^2 = 14\,m^2$

Exercise 4.5

Find the area of the shaded part of each shape.

1

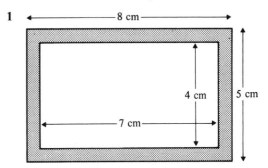

2

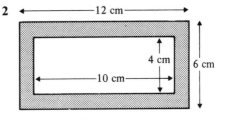

3

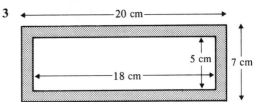

4

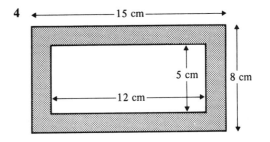

40

5

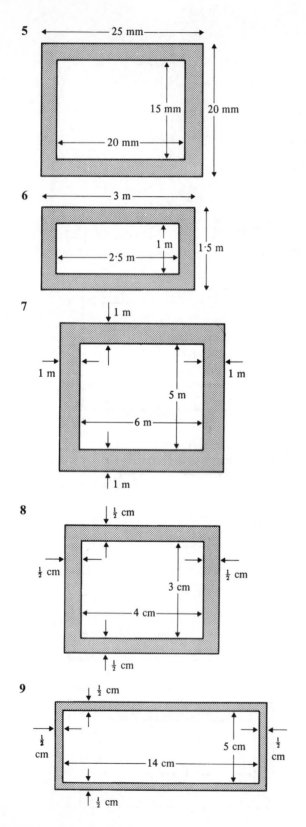

25 mm
15 mm
20 mm
20 mm

6

3 m
1 m
2·5 m
1·5 m

7

1 m
1 m
1 m
5 m
6 m
1 m

8

½ cm
½ cm
½ cm
3 cm
4 cm
½ cm

9

½ cm
½ cm
5 cm
14 cm
½ cm
½ cm

10

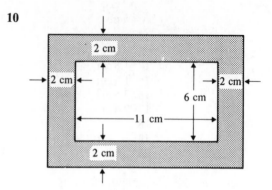

2 cm
2 cm
2 cm
6 cm
11 cm
2 cm

11

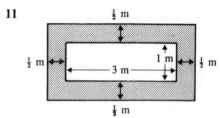

½ m
½ m
1 m
½ m
3 m
½ m

12

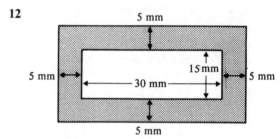

5 mm
5 mm
15 mm
5 mm
30 mm
5 mm

Example 6

Find the area of the shaded part of each shape.

a

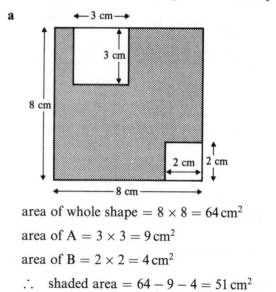

3 cm
3 cm
8 cm
2 cm | 2 cm
8 cm

area of whole shape $= 8 \times 8 = 64\,\text{cm}^2$

area of A $= 3 \times 3 = 9\,\text{cm}^2$

area of B $= 2 \times 2 = 4\,\text{cm}^2$

$\therefore$ shaded area $= 64 - 9 - 4 = 51\,\text{cm}^2$

b

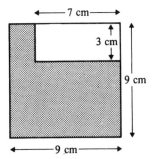

area of parallelogram $ABCD = 7 \times 4 = 28\,\text{cm}^2$

area of triangle $DTC = \frac{1}{2} \times 7 \times 4 = 14\,\text{cm}^2$

$\therefore$ shaded area $= 28 - 14 = 14\,\text{cm}^2$

c

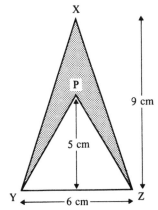

area of triangle $XYZ = \frac{1}{2} \times 6 \times 9 = 27\,\text{cm}^2$

area of triangle $PYZ = \frac{1}{2} \times 6 \times 5 = 15\,\text{cm}^2$

$\therefore$ shaded area $= 27 - 15 = 12\,\text{cm}^2$

Exercise 4.6

Find the area of the shaded part in each shape.

1

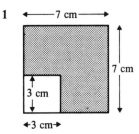

2

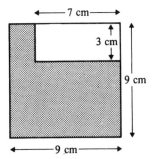

3

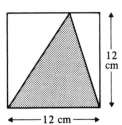

4

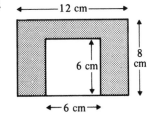

5

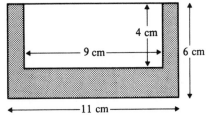

6

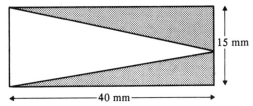

7

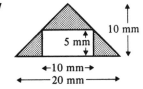

42

8

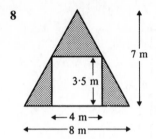

7 m

3·5 m

4 m

8 m

9

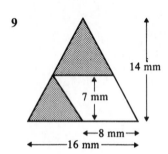

14 mm

7 mm

8 mm

16 mm

10

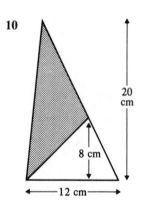

20 cm

8 cm

12 cm

11

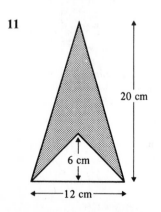

20 cm

6 cm

12 cm

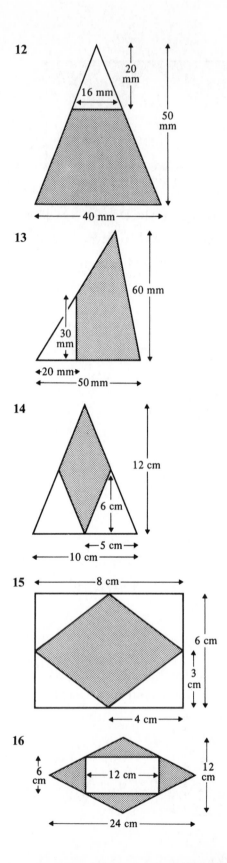

12

20 mm

16 mm

50 mm

40 mm

13

60 mm

30 mm

20 mm

50 mm

14

12 cm

6 cm

5 cm

10 cm

15

8 cm

6 cm

3 cm

4 cm

16

6 cm

12 cm

12 cm

24 cm

Example 7

One wall of a living room is to be covered with wallpaper costing £3.50 per m². The dimensions are shown in the diagram.
Find the cost of the wallpaper.

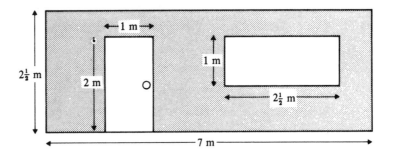

area of wall $= 7\,\text{m} \times 2\tfrac{1}{2}\,\text{m} = 17\tfrac{1}{2}\,\text{m}^2$

area of door $= 2\,\text{m} \times 1\,\text{m} = 2\,\text{m}^2$

area of window $= 2\tfrac{1}{2}\,\text{m} \times 1\,\text{m} = 2\tfrac{1}{2}\,\text{m}^2$

$\therefore$ area to be covered with wallpaper

$$= 17\tfrac{1}{2}\,\text{m}^2 - 2\,\text{m}^2 - 2\tfrac{1}{2}\,\text{m}^2 = 13\,\text{m}^2$$

so cost $= £3.50 \times 13 = £45.50$

Exercise 4.7

1 A bedroom wall has one window. All the dimensions are shown in the diagram. Find the area of wallpaper required to cover this wall.

2 The diagram shows the plan of a loft which is to be insulated. Find the area of insulating material required.

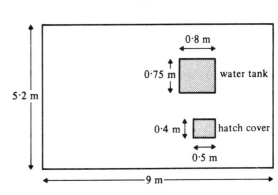

3 The diagram shows the dimensions of a yard.
Find
a the area of the yard
b the number of paving slabs of dimensions $0.8\,m \times 0.5\,m$ that are required for covering the yard.

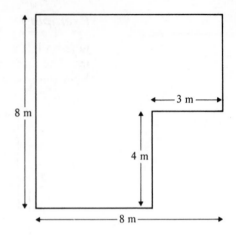

4 A square lawn is bordered by a shingle path.
Find
a the area of the path
b the number of bags of shingle required to cover the path if it is supplied in $50\,kg$ bags and $1\,m^2$ of path requires $40\,kg$ of shingle.

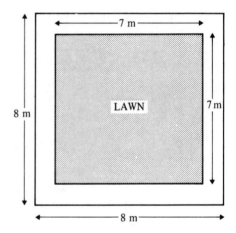

5 The ends of a rabbit hutch are to be made from two pieces of wood measuring $50\,cm \times 50\,cm$. The dimensions are shown in the diagram.
Find the area of each of the ends.

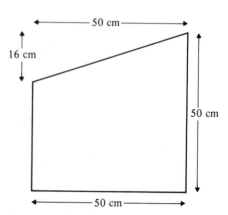

6 An arrow for a signpost is to be cut from a sheet of metal measuring 20 cm × 20 cm.

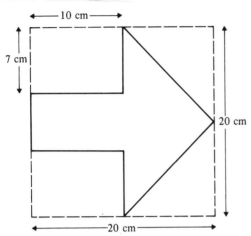

The dimensions are shown in the diagram. Find the area of the arrow.

7 The diagram shows a piece of metal which is to be used for making a saw blade. Find its area.

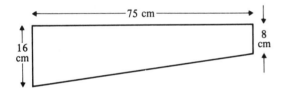

8 The diagram shows the end of a terrace of houses. Find the area of this end wall.

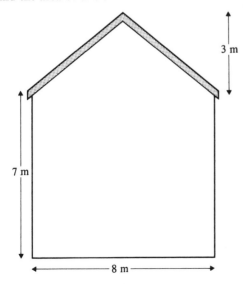

9 Find the area of the spinning dice.

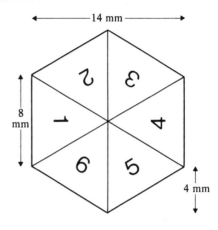

10 The diagram below shows a piece of wood which has been cut for making the deck of a toy boat. Find its area.

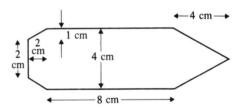

11 The diagram shows a joiner's tri-square. Find
   a the area of the metal blade
   b the area of the wooden handle
   c the area of the blade which is enclosed by the handle in both mm² and cm².

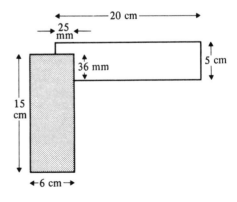

Unit 5 Equations and inequalities

Negative numbers

Example 1

Copy and complete the table.

×	3	2	1	0	−1	−2	−3
3	9			0			
2	6		2	0	−2		−6
1		2					
0				0	0	0	
−1	−3		−1	0			
−2				0			
−3			−3	0			

Here is the completed table.

×	3	2	1	0	−1	−2	−3	
3	9	6	3	0	−3	−6	−9	
2	6	4	2	0	−2	−4	−6	**a**
1	3	2	1	0	−1	−2	−3	
0	0	0	0	0	0	0	0	
−1	−3	−2	−1	0	1	2	3	
−2	−6	−4	−2	0	2	4	6	**b**
−3	−9	−6	−3	0	3	6	9	**c**

Exercise 5.1

Copy and complete each table.

1

×	10	5	0	−5	−10
10					
5					
0					
−5					
−10					

2

×	6	3	0	−3	−6
6					
3					
0					
−3					
−6					

3

×	4	2	0	−2	−4
8					
4					
0					
−4					
−8					

4

×	8	4	0	−4	−8
6					
3					
0					
−3					
−6					

5

×	5	2	0	−2	−5
5					
2					
0					
−2					
−5					

6

×	−1	−2	−3	−4	−5
−1					
0					
1					
2					
3					

Look again at the answer to Example 1.

From line **a** $2 \times 3 = 6$

From line **b** $-2 \times -3 = 6$

From line **a** $2 \times -3 = -6$

From line **c** $-3 \times 2 = -6$

When the signs are the same, the product is positive.
When the signs are different, the product is negative.

Example 2

Find the value of the following.

a -4×-6 **b** -2×4
c 2×-8

a $-4 \times -6 = 24$
Both signs are the same.

b $-2 \times 4 = -8$
The two signs are different.

c $2 \times -8 = -16$
The two signs are different.

Example 3

Find the value of the following.

a $-2x \times 6$ **b** $-3a \times -2a$
c $3a \times -2b$

a $-2x \times 6 \quad = -2 \times x \times 6$
$\qquad\qquad = -2 \times 6 \times x = -12x$

b $-3a \times -2a = -3 \times a \times -2 \times a$
$\qquad\qquad = -3 \times -2 \times a \times a = 6a^2$

c $3a \times -2b \quad = 3 \times a \times -2 \times b$
$\qquad\qquad = 3 \times -2 \times a \times b = -6ab$

Exercise 5.2

Find the value of the following products.

1 12×5	**2** 4×2
3 3×6	**4** -6×-5
5 -8×-4	**6** -7×-6
7 -12×-3	**8** -8×-1
9 -6×-2	**10** -4×-1
11 -2×-8	**12** -2×-12
13 5×-3	**14** 8×-4
15 9×-6	**16** 12×-7
17 6×-1	**18** 10×-2
19 12×-1	**20** 3×-2
21 2×-4	**22** -6×4
23 -7×5	**24** -12×6
25 -11×3	**26** $-4 \times 2\frac{1}{2}$
27 $-10 \times 3\frac{1}{2}$	**28** $-8 \times 2\frac{1}{2}$
29 $-2\frac{1}{2} \times 6$	**30** $-1\frac{1}{2} \times 8$
31 $3a \times 2$	**32** $5a \times 4b$
33 $6a \times 5a$	**34** $-5x \times -3$
35 $-7y \times -4$	**36** $-12z \times -6$
37 $-4 \times -2a$	**38** $-7 \times -5b$
39 $-5m \times -3n$	**40** $-8p \times -5q$
41 $-7x \times -4x$	**42** $-9y \times -3y$
43 $7x \times -3$	**44** $9y \times -5$
45 $11z \times -4$	**46** $8 \times -3a$
47 $6 \times -6b$	**48** $7u \times -6v$
49 $12p \times -5q$	**50** $8m \times -4m$
51 $9n \times -7n$	**52** $-9p \times 4$
53 $-7q \times 5$	**54** $-10r \times 7$
55 $-6a \times 3$	**56** $-12b \times 9$
57 $-8x \times 7y$	**58** $-11m \times 5n$
59 $-9t \times 8t$	**60** $-12u \times u$

Reminder
Division by a number is the same as multiplication by the inverse of that number.

$$8 \div 4 = 8 \times \tfrac{1}{4}$$

So the same sign rules apply to division as to multiplication.

When the signs are the same, the answer is positive.
When the signs are different, the answer is negative.

Example 4

Work out the following.

a $-6 \div -2$ **b** $-8 \div 4$
c $12 \div -6$ **d** $6x \div 3x$

a $-6 \div -2 = 3$
Both signs are the same.

b $-8 \div 4 = -2$
The two signs are different.

c $12 \div -6 = -2$
The two signs are different.

d $6x \div 3x = \dfrac{6x}{3x}$

$\qquad\qquad = \dfrac{{}^{2}\cancel{6} \times \cancel{x}^{1}}{{}_{1}\cancel{3} \times \cancel{x}_{1}} = 2$

Exercise 5.3

Work out the following

1 $15 \div 3$	**2** $8 \div 2$
3 $20 \div 5$	**4** $-12 \div -4$
5 $-24 \div -6$	**6** $-28 \div -4$
7 $-48 \div -3$	**8** $-70 \div -5$
9 $-9 \div -1$	**10** $-16 \div -4$
11 $-24 \div -4$	**12** $60 \div -12$
13 $36 \div -9$	**14** $56 \div -7$
15 $42 \div -6$	**16** $60 \div -4$
17 $72 \div -6$	**18** $99 \div -11$
19 $72 \div -8$	**20** $15 \div -5$
21 $36 \div -12$	**22** $-40 \div 8$
23 $-36 \div 4$	**24** $-81 \div 9$
25 $-42 \div 3$	**26** $-91 \div 7$
27 $-150 \div 2$	**28** $-18 \div 4$
29 $-35 \div 10$	**30** $-50 \div 20$
31 $10a \div 2a$	**32** $12a \div 3a$

33 $18a \div 3$

35 $-27x \div -3$

37 $-36z \div -9$

39 $-45b \div -9b$

41 $-56u \div -7u$

43 $-63n \div -9n$

45 $32y \div -4$

47 $36u \div -6u$

49 $42a \div -7a$

51 $72x \div -12x$

53 $-40a \div 5$

55 $-36m \div 12m$

57 $-21p \div 3p$

59 $-24c^2 \div 2c$

34 $15a \div 5$

36 $-35y \div -7$

38 $-28a \div -4a$

40 $-54x \div -6x$

42 $-72m \div -8m$

44 $20x \div -5$

46 $54t \div -9t$

48 $48v \div -12v$

50 $25c \div -5c$

52 $60y \div -20y$

54 $-27b \div 9$

56 $-80n \div 20n$

58 $-49rs \div 7r$

60 $-120d^2 \div 12d$

a $2a = 2 \times a = 2 \times -2 = -4$

b $3b + c = (3b) + c$
$$= (3 \times b) + c$$
$$= (3 \times 3) + -4$$
$$= 9 - 4 = 5$$

c $4a - 3c = (4a) - (3c)$
$$= (4 \times a) - (3 \times c)$$
$$= (4 \times -2) - (3 \times -4)$$
$$= -8 - -12$$
$$= -8 + 12 = 4$$

Substitution

Reminder

$$3a = 3 \times a$$

$$ab = a \times b$$

$$a^2 = a \times a$$

$$5x^3 = 5 \times x^3 = 5 \times x \times x \times x$$

$$d^2e = d^2 \times e = d \times d \times e$$

Exercise 5.4

Find the value of the following if $a = 4$, $b = 2$.

1 $a + b$

4 $7a$

7 ab

10 b^2

13 $2a + b$

16 $a - 2b$

19 $a^2 + b^2$

22 a^2b

2 $a - b$

5 $4b$

8 ba

11 $2ab$

14 $a + 2b$

17 $2a + 2b$

20 $2a^2$

23 ab^2

3 $2a$

6 $10b$

9 a^2

12 $4ab$

15 $4a - b$

18 $3a - 4b$

21 $3b^2$

24 a^2b^2

Find the value of the following if $p = 5$, $q = 3$.

25 $p + q$

28 $5q$

31 pq

34 p^2

37 $2p + 3q$

40 p^2q

43 q^3

46 $p^3 - p^2$

26 $p - q$

29 $2q + p$

32 $2pq$

35 q^2

38 $3p - 2q$

41 pq^2

44 $2q^3$

47 p^2q^2

27 $4p$

30 $4p - q$

33 $5pq$

36 $5q^2$

39 $p^2 - q^2$

42 p^3

45 $2p^2 + q^2$

48 $2p^2q^2$

Example 5

If $a = -2$, $b = 3$, $c = -4$, find the value of

a $2a$

b $3b + c$

c $4a - 3c$

Exercise 5.5

If $a = 3$, $b = -2$, $c = -4$, find the value of

1 $3a$

4 $4b$

7 $2c$

2 $2a + b$

5 $a + 4b$

8 $b + 2c$

3 $3a + c$

6 $a + 3c$

9 $c + 2b$

If $p = 2$, $q = -3$, $r = -5$, find the value of

10 $5p$

13 $6q$

16 $9r$

11 $4p + 2q$

14 $2p + 3q$

17 $3q + r$

12 $8p + 3r$

15 $3p + 2r$

18 $3r + 2q$

If $x = 2$, $y = -3$, $z = -4$, find the value of

19 $7x$

22 $5y$

25 $4z$

20 $3x - y$

23 $y - 2z$

26 $2y - z$

21 $2x - z$

24 $z - 5y$

27 $3z - y$

If $a = 3$, $b = -2$, $c = -5$, find the value of

28 $6a$

31 $8b$

34 $12c$

29 $2a - 3b$

32 $5b - 3c$

35 $12b - 4c$

30 $3a - c$

33 $2c - 8b$

36 $3c - 5b$

Example 6

a Find x if $12x = -60$
$12x = -60$
So $12 \times x = -60$
$\therefore \qquad x = -5$
because $12 \times -5 = -60$

b Find a if $-4a = 4$
$-4a = 4$
So $-4 \times a = 4$
$\therefore \qquad a = -1$
because $-4 \times -1 = 4$

c Find b if $-2b = -8$
$-2b = -8$
So $-2 \times b = -8$
$\therefore \qquad b = 4$
because $-2 \times 4 = -8$

Exercise 5.6

1 Find x if $5x = 35$	2 Find y if $9y = 27$
3 Find z if $12z = 48$	4 Find a if $3a = -18$
5 Find b if $5b = -30$	6 Find c if $7c = -28$
7 Find d if $6d = -48$	8 Find m if $9m - 54$
9 Find n if $8n = -64$	10 Find p if $2p = -24$
11 Find q if $4q = -80$	12 Find r if $10r = -90$
13 Find x if $-4x = 36$	14 Find y if $-6y = 42$
15 Find z if $-8z = 40$	16 Find a if $-3a = 27$
17 Find b if $-5b = 45$	18 Find c if $-7c = 56$
19 Find d if $-9d = 81$	20 Find m if $-12m = 72$
21 Find n if $-20n = 100$	22 Find p if $-5p = -25$
23 Find q if $-8q = -32$	24 Find r if $-6r = -30$
25 Find t if $-4t = -24$	26 Find u if $-3u = -60$
27 Find v if $-7v = -35$	28 Find x if $-9x = -36$
29 Find y if $-12y = -96$	30 Find z if $-11z = -132$

Example 7

If $a = 5$, $b = -4$, $c = -2$ and $d = 0$, find the value of

a ab **b** $3bc$ **c** $2bcd$

a $ab = a \times b = 5 \times -4 = -20$

b $3bc = 3 \times bc$
$= 3 \times b \times c$
$= 3 \times -4 \times -2$
$= -12 \times -2 = 24$

c $2bcd = 2 \times bcd$
$= 2 \times b \times c \times d$
$= 2 \times -4 \times -2 \times 0$
$= -8 \times -2 \times 0$
$= 16 \times 0$
$= 0$

Exercise 5.7

If $a = 3$, $b = -2$, $c = -4$ and $d = 0$, find the value of

1 ab	2 ac	3 bc	4 ad
5 cd	6 $2ab$	7 $4bc$	8 $10ad$
9 $5cd$	10 $3ac$	11 abc	12 abd
13 acd	14 bcd	15 $abcd$	16 $2abc$
17 $5abc$	18 $3acd$	19 $10bcd$	20 $5abcd$

If $a = -2$, $b = -3$, $c = -6$, $d = -1$, find the value of

21 ab	22 ac	23 ad	24 bc
25 bd	26 cd	27 $2ab$	28 $3bc$
29 $4cd$	30 $5ad$	31 abc	32 bcd
33 acd	34 abd	35 $abcd$	36 $2bcd$
37 $2abc$	38 $2acd$	39 $-2acd$	40 $-5abc$

Example 8

If $p = -3$ and $q = -2$, find the value of

a p^3 **b** $3q^2$ **c** pq^2 **d** $(pq)^2$

a $p^3 = p \times p \times p$
$= -3 \times -3 \times -3$
$= 9 \times -3 = -27$

b $3q^2 = 3 \times q^2$
$= 3 \times q \times q$
$= 3 \times -2 \times -2$
$= -6 \times -2 = 12$

c $pq^2 = p \times q^2$
$= p \times q \times q$
$= -3 \times -2 \times -2$
$= 6 \times -2 = -12$

d $(pq)^2 = pq \times pq$
$= p \times q \times p \times q$
$= -3 \times -2 \times -3 \times -2$
$= 6 \times -3 \times -2$
$= -18 \times -2$
$= 36$

Exercise 5.8

If $a = -2$ and $b = -4$, find the value of

1 a^2	2 $5b^2$	3 a^3
4 a^2b	5 ab^2	6 $(ab)^2$

If $p = -3$ and $q = -1$, find the value of

7 $4p^2$	8 $6q^2$	9 $2p^3$
10 $3p^2q$	11 $4pq^2$	12 $5(pq)^2$

If $m = 3$ and $n = -2$, find the value of

13 $5m^2$	14 $3n^2$	15 $4n^3$
16 $2m^2n$	17 $5mn^2$	18 $2(mn)^2$

If $x = 4$ and $y = -3$, find the value of

19 $2x^2$	20 $6y^2$	21 $3y^3$
22 x^2y	23 $2xy^2$	24 $(xy)^2$

If $u = -2$ and $v = 3$, find the value of

25 $7u^2$	26 $11v^2$	27 $5u^3$
28 $3u^2v$	29 $2uv^2$	30 $3(uv)^2$

Simplifying

$$2 \times 3 = 3 \times 2$$

In the same way,

$$a \times b = b \times a$$

$$ab = ba$$

So $ab + ba = 2ab$

Example 9

Simplify the following by collecting like terms.

a $3a - 2b - 5a + 5b$
b $2ab + 3ba - 4ab$

a $3a - 2b - 5a + 5b$
$= 3a - 5a - 2b + 5b$
$= -2a + 3b$
$= 3b - 2a$

b $2ab + 3ba - 4ab$
$= 2ab + 3ab - 4ab$
$= 5ab - 4ab$
$= ab$

Exercise 5.9

Simplify the following by collecting like terms.

1	$4a + 3a + 2a$	**2**	$6b + 4b + b$
3	$9c + 3c - 2c$	**4**	$2d + 5d - 4d$
5	$5m + 3m - 4m$	**6**	$7n + 2n - 8n$
7	$9p - 4p - 2p$	**8**	$12q - 6q - 3q$
9	$10r - 3r - r$	**10**	$11s - 6s - 4s$
11	$3x + 7y + 2x$	**12**	$8u + 2v + u$
13	$6a + 5b - 2a$	**14**	$7c + 3d - 5c$
15	$9m + 4n - m$	**16**	$5z + 7z^2 - 3z$
17	$10t + 8t^2 - 5t$	**18**	$3a + 2b + 6a + 5b$
19	$5c + 3d + 7c + 4d$	**20**	$2m + 7n + 9m + n$
21	$5p + 8q + 2p - 3q$	**22**	$7u + 5v + u - 2v$
23	$9x + 6y + 3x - 5y$	**24**	$8a + 9b - 2a - 4b$
25	$12c + 10d - 9c - 3d$	**26**	$9z^2 + 8z - 7z^2 - 3z$
27	$11t^2 + 10t - t^2 - 9t$	**28**	$5a + 4b - 2a - 6b$
29	$8c + 5d - 3c - 9d$	**30**	$10m + 3n - 8m - 6n$
31	$12z^2 + 4z - 2z^2 - 9z$	**32**	$8t^2 + 6t - t^2 - 10t$
33	$9p + q - 6p - 3q$	**34**	$11r + 5s - 7r - 6s$
35	$6u + 10v - 5u - 11v$	**36**	$3a + 9b - 5a - 4b$
37	$5c + 10d - 9c - 6d$	**38**	$4x + 12y - 7x - 8y$
39	$u + 11v - 3u - 6v$	**40**	$z^2 + 12z - 5z^2 - 9z$

41	$2t^2 + 5t - 3t^2 - t$	**42**	$6m + 2n - 7m - n$
43	$5p - 4q - 2p - 3q$	**44**	$8x - 5y - 3x - 3y$
45	$10a - 8b - 5a - 4b$	**46**	$12c - 7d - c - 3d$
47	$11m - 8n - 9m - n$	**48**	$2p - 9q - p - q$
49	$5ab + 4ba - 2ab$	**50**	$8cd + 2dc - 5cd$
51	$7mn + 5nm - 9mn$	**52**	$6rs + 5sr - 10rs$
53	$9xy - 3yx - 4xy$	**54**	$12uv - 5vu - 2uv$
55	$10mn - nm - 4mn$	**56**	$9xy - 6yx + 4xy$
57	$12pq - 8qp + 3pq$	**58**	$10uv - 5vu + uv$
59	$4ab - 7ba + 5ab$	**60**	$4cd - 5dc + cd$

$$2a = a + a$$

In the same way,

$$2(a + b) = (a + b) + (a + b) = a + b + a + b$$
$$= a + a + b + b$$
$$= 2a + 2b$$

Also,

$$3(x - y) = x - y + x - y + x - y$$
$$= x + x + x - y - y - y$$
$$= 3x - 3y$$

Each term inside the bracket has been multiplied by the number outside the bracket.

Example 10

Remove the brackets to simplify the following.

a $6(x + 2)$ **b** $-3(x + 3)$
c $-2(x - y)$ **d** $3(2x + 3y)$

a $6(x + 2) = 6x + 12$

b $-3(x + 3) = -3x - 9$
because $-3 \times 3 = -9$

c $-2(x - y) = -2x + 2y$
because $-2 \times -1y = +2y$

d $3(2x + 3y) = 6x + 9y$

Exercise 5.10

Remove the brackets to simplify the following.

1	$4(x + 2)$	**2**	$5(y + 3)$
3	$3(z + 4)$	**4**	$6(a + b)$
5	$2(p - 3)$	**6**	$4(q - 2)$
7	$3(r - 1)$	**8**	$5(c - d)$
9	$-3(a - 4)$	**10**	$-5(b - 2)$
11	$-4(c - 3)$	**12**	$-2(u - v)$
13	$-3(m + 2)$	**14**	$-4(n + 5)$
15	$-6(p + q)$	**16**	$2(3x + 2y)$

17 $4(2m + 5n)$
19 $3(u + 4v)$
21 $3(5c - 2d)$
23 $5(x - 5y)$
25 $-4(5r - 4s)$
27 $-2(a - 8b)$
29 $-3(3m + n)$

18 $5(3p + q)$
20 $4(3a - 4b)$
22 $6(2m - n)$
24 $-3(2p - 3q)$
26 $-8(3u - v)$
28 $-5(6x + 5y)$
30 $-7(c + 5d)$

Example 11

For the following, remove the brackets, then simplify by collecting like terms.

a $4(x + y) - 3x$ **b** $3(a + b) - 2(b - a)$

a $4(x + y) - 3x$
$= 4x + 4y - 3x$
$= 4x - 3x + 4y$
$= x + 4y$

b $3(a + b) - 2(b - a)$
$= 3a + 3b - 2b + 2a$
$= 5a + b$

Exercise 5.11

For each question remove the brackets, then simplify by collecting like terms.

1 $3(x + y) + 2x$
3 $4(a + b) + a$
5 $6(m + n) - 2m$
7 $2(x + y) + 5y$
9 $8(c + d) - 6d$
11 $2(a + b) + 3(a + b)$
13 $6(p + q) + 5(p - q)$
15 $5(b + c) + 8(b - c)$
17 $3(a - b) + 4(a + b)$
19 $4(y - z) + 6(y - z)$
21 $7(p - q) + 2(q - p)$
23 $7(c - d) - 5(c + d)$
25 $4(p - q) - (p + q)$
27 $6(x + y) - 4(x - y)$
29 $10(m - n) - 2(m - n)$

2 $2(u + v) + 4u$
4 $5(c + d) - 3c$
6 $4(p + q) + 3q$
8 $6(a + b) - 2b$
10 $5(m + n) - 4n$
12 $4(m + n) + 2(m - n)$
14 $4(u + v) + 6(u - v)$
16 $4(x - y) + 7(x + y)$
18 $5(c - d) + 2(c + d)$
20 $5(m - n) + 3(n - m)$
22 $5(x + y) - 2(x + y)$
24 $6(m - n) - 3(m + n)$
26 $5(u + v) - 3(u - v)$
28 $4(a + b) - 3(a - b)$
30 $5(p - q) - 4(p - q)$

Solving equations

$$3x + 5 = 14$$

A relationship like this is called a simple *linear equation*.
Finding the value of x (which makes both sides of this equal) is called *solving* the equation.

For this equation, $x = 3$.
Both sides of an equation must always be equal. So, if one side is changed, then the other side of the equation must also be changed in the same way.

If $3x = 9$
then $x = 3$,

and this result is obtained by dividing both sides by 3.

If $4a = 3$
then $a = \frac{3}{4}$;

both sides are divided by 4.

Example 12

Solve the following equations.

a $4x = 20$ **b** $3b = -9$
c $-2a = 10$ **d** $-2a = -12$

a $4x = 20$
Divide both sides by 4.
$$\frac{4x}{4} = \frac{20}{4}$$
$\Rightarrow$ $x = 5$

b $3b = -9$
Divide both sides by 3.
$$\frac{3b}{3} = \frac{-9}{3}$$
$\Rightarrow$ $b = -3$

c $-2a = 10$
Divide both sides by -2.
$$\frac{-2a}{-2} = \frac{10}{-2}$$
$\Rightarrow$ $a = -5$

d $-2a = -12$
Divide both sides by -2.
$$\frac{-2a}{-2} = \frac{-12}{-2}$$
$\Rightarrow$ $a = 6$

Exercise 5.12

Solve the following equations.

1 $3x = 12$		**2** $5x = 30$
3 $4x = 28$		**4** $6y = 48$
5 $2y = 30$		**6** $3z = 48$
7 $5a = 90$		**8** $4b = 64$
9 $6c = 84$		**10** $7d = 105$
11 $3x = -54$		**12** $5x = -65$
13 $4y = -64$		**14** $8z = -104$
15 $7t = -112$		**16** $9a = -126$
17 $6b = -108$		**18** $5c = -120$
19 $6m = -150$		**20** $8n = -160$
21 $-4x = 68$		**22** $-6x = 96$
23 $-5y = 95$		**24** $-3y = 87$
25 $-7z = 98$		**26** $-8t = 120$
27 $-6a = 102$		**28** $-9b = 135$
29 $-7c = 133$		**30** $-6d = 132$
31 $-5x = -75$		**32** $-2x = -36$
33 $-3y = -72$		**34** $-4y = -84$
35 $-7z = -119$		**36** $-4a = -100$
37 $-8b = -144$		**38** $-9c = -153$
39 $-6u = -150$		**40** $-7v = -182$

If $\quad x + 5 = 23$
then $\quad x = 18$

Here 5 has been subtracted from both sides of the equation.

If $\quad x - 4 = 14$
then $\quad x = 18$

Here 4 has been added to both sides of the equation.

If $\quad 4a + 10 = 22$
then $\quad 4a = 12$
$\Rightarrow \quad\quad a = 3$

Here 10 has been subtracted from both sides; then both sides have been divided by 4.

Example 13

Solve the following equations.

a $x + 6 = 9$ $\quad\quad$ **b** $3x + 5 = 11$
c $4a - 10 = 22$

a $x + 6 = 9$
$\Rightarrow \quad x = 3$

Here 6 is subtracted from both sides.

b $3x + 5 = 11$
$\Rightarrow \quad 3x = 6 \quad$ (subtract 5 from both sides)
$\Rightarrow \quad\; x = 2 \quad$ (divide both sides by 3)

c $4a - 10 = 22$
$\Rightarrow \quad 4a = 32 \quad$ (add 10 to both sides)
$\Rightarrow \quad\; a = 8 \quad$ (divide both sides by 4)

Exercise 5.13

Solve the following equations.

1 $x + 5 = 7$		**2** $x + 3 = 9$
3 $y + 4 = 8$		**4** $y + 6 = 7$
5 $z + 2 = 10$		**6** $z + 8 = 12$
7 $t + 5 = 11$		**8** $t + 7 = 19$
9 $a + 9 = 16$		**10** $b + 6 = 15$
11 $x - 3 = 4$		**12** $x - 2 = 6$
13 $y - 4 = 5$		**14** $y - 1 = 8$
15 $z - 5 = 3$		**16** $z - 9 = 1$
17 $a - 8 = 4$		**18** $a - 6 = 8$
19 $b - 8 = 10$		**20** $c - 7 = 13$
21 $3x + 4 = 16$		**22** $5x + 2 = 17$
23 $4y + 3 = 19$		**24** $2y + 5 = 15$
25 $8z + 9 = 25$		**26** $6a + 7 = 25$
27 $7b + 8 = 36$		**28** $5c + 7 = 32$
29 $9m + 5 = 41$		**30** $8n + 5 = 53$
31 $6x + 7 = 13$		**32** $3y + 8 = 29$
33 $8t + 9 = 41$		**34** $3z + 8 = 17$
35 $4a + 11 = 19$		**36** $5b + 13 = 38$
37 $7c + 11 = 60$		**38** $9d + 16 = 34$
39 $12p + 13 = 85$		**40** $11q + 16 = 60$
41 $3x - 11 = 10$		**42** $4x - 9 = 3$
43 $6y - 5 = 1$		**44** $7y - 2 = 12$
45 $6z - 7 = 11$		**46** $2t - 3 = 15$
47 $3a - 5 = 16$		**48** $5b - 8 = 17$
49 $4c - 5 = 19$		**50** $8d - 9 = 15$
51 $5m - 7 = 18$		**52** $7n - 8 = 27$
53 $9p - 8 = 28$		**54** $6q - 7 = 47$
55 $8x - 12 = 20$		**56** $7x - 10 = 25$
57 $6y - 15 = 21$		**58** $9y - 20 = 34$
59 $12z - 14 = 22$		**60** $11t - 15 = 40$

Often like terms have to be collected before an equation can be solved.

Example 14

Solve the following equations.

a $6x - 3x + 2x = 10$
b $5a + 5 + 3a = 21$

a $6x - 3x + 2x = 10$

$\Rightarrow \quad 3x + 2x = 10$

$\Rightarrow \qquad\quad 5x = 10$ (collect like terms)

So, $\qquad\qquad x = 2$ (divide by 5)

b $5a + 5 + 3a = 21$

$\Rightarrow \quad 8a + 5 = 21$ (collect like terms)

$\Rightarrow \qquad 8a = 16$ (subtract 5)

$\Rightarrow \qquad\; a = 2$ (divide by 8)

Exercise 5.14

Solve the following equations.

1 $6x + 3x + 2x = 33$	2 $5y + 2y + y = 56$
3 $3p + 4p - 2p = 20$	4 $5q + 3q - 6q = 16$
5 $6r + 4r - r = 36$	6 $8s + 2s - 9s = 12$
7 $8a - 3a + 2a = 21$	8 $9b - 6b + 4b = 35$
9 $12c - 5c + 2c = 54$	10 $5d - d + 4d = 40$
11 $9m - 3m - 2m = 8$	12 $12n - 2n - 7n = 15$
13 $11u - 4u - u = 30$	14 $15v - 5v - 9v = 7$
15 $4a + 7 + 2a = 25$	16 $6b + 5 + 3b = 50$
17 $3c + 9 + 5c = 17$	18 $7d + 15 + d = 55$
19 $3p - 8 + 2p = 22$	20 $5q - 3 + 3q = 29$
21 $4r - 11 + 5r = 25$	22 $9s - 12 + 2s = 21$
23 $9x + 5 - 3x = 23$	24 $12y + 7 - 4y = 63$
25 $20t + 9 - 12t = 33$	26 $11z + 15 - 7z = 35$
27 $9m - 7 - 3m = 5$	28 $12n - 8 - 5n = 13$
29 $11v - 12 - 4v = 9$	30 $15u - 15 - 7u = 17$

Solving inequalities

$$3x + 5 > 14$$

A relationship like this is called a *linear inequality*.

It means that three times the number x, plus 5, always gives an answer greater than 14.

We *solve* the inequality by simplifying it until we have a statement about x itself.

We use rules like those used to solve equations.

$$3x + 5 > 14$$

Subtract 5 from both sides

$\Rightarrow \quad 3x > 9$

Divide both sides by 3

$\Rightarrow \quad \dfrac{3x}{3} > \dfrac{9}{3}$

$\Rightarrow \quad x > 3$

So, our original relationship $3x + 5 > 14$ can be simplified to $x > 3$, or, in words, x is any number greater than 3.

The solution of an inequality is often represented on a number line like this.

The hollow 'blob' shows that the number 3 is not part of the solution.

Example 15

Solve the inequality $4q + 5 \leqslant 1$ and illustrate the solution on a number line.

$$4q + 5 \leqslant 1$$

Subtract 5 from both sides

$\Rightarrow \quad 4q \leqslant -4$

Divide both sides by 4

$\Rightarrow \quad q \leqslant -1$

Here, the solid 'blob' shows that the number -1 is part of the solution.

Exercise 5.15

Solve the following inequalities and illustrate the solutions on number lines.

1 $x + 5 \leqslant 8$	2 $m + 2 > 4$
3 $a - 1 < 0$	4 $y - 2 \geqslant 1$
5 $2x \leqslant 8$	6 $3p > 15$
7 $2t + 1 < 5$	8 $3d - 5 \geqslant 7$
9 $x + 4 \leqslant 1$	10 $f + 4 > 1$
11 $2z < -4$	12 $3e \leqslant -9$
13 $10q > -20$	14 $w - 4 > -4$
15 $e - 7 \geqslant -7$	16 $r - 11 \geqslant -11$
17 $t + 3 < 3$	18 $2y + 3 > 1$
19 $u + 6 \leqslant 2$	20 $3p - 2 > -8$
21 $5a + 7 < 2$	22 $3s + 20 \geqslant 5$
23 $2d - 1 \leqslant -7$	24 $2f + 5 > -15$

You can multiply or divide both sides of an inequality by any number, but if you multiply or divide by a negative number you must reverse the direction of the inequality sign.

Example 16

Solve the inequality $6 - 4m < 19$ and illustrate the solution on a number line.

$$6 - 4m < 18$$

subtract 6 from both sides

$$\Rightarrow \quad -4m < 12$$

divide both sides by -4 and reverse the sign

$$\Rightarrow \quad m > -3$$

Exercise 5.16

Solve the following inequalities and illustrate the solutions on number lines.

1	$6 - x > 8$	**2**	$8 - x < 6$
3	$10 - x > 7$	**4**	$7 - x < 7$
5	$5 - x > 4$	**6**	$4 - x < 5$
7	$3 - x > 9$	**8**	$9 - x < 3$
9	$-2x > 4$	**10**	$-3x < 15$
11	$-2x > -4$	**12**	$-3x < -15$
13	$-6x < 12$	**14**	$-6x < -12$
15	$-8x < 24$	**16**	$-8x > -24$
17	$8 - 2x < 10$	**18**	$10 - 2x > 8$
19	$5 - 3x < 20$	**20**	$20 - 3x > 5$

Graphs of inequalities

On the graph illustrated, any ordered pair that gives the position of a point in the shaded region A will have a y-value that is less than 3.

The shaded area A is therefore the region $y < 3$.

The non-shaded area B is the region $y > 3$.

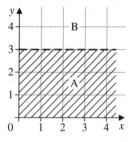

In this graph the shaded area B includes the line $x = 4$; B is the region $x \geqslant 4$.

The non-shaded area A is the region $x \leqslant 4$.

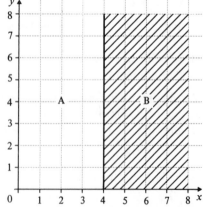

When drawing or describing regions on a graph remember the following two points.

(1) A broken line indicates that no point in the region lies on the line.
(2) An unbroken line indicates that all points on the line are included in the region.

Example 17

Describe the following shaded regions.

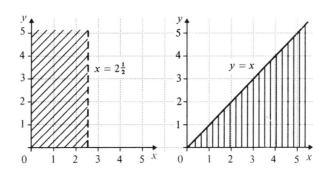

a The region is $x < 2\frac{1}{2}$

b The region is $y \leqslant x$.

Example 18

Illustrate the following regions.

a $y \leqslant 2$

b $x + y > 4$

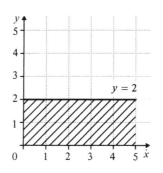 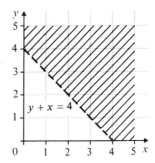

Exercise 5.17

Describe the following shaded regions.

1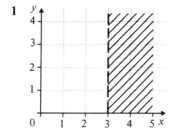

2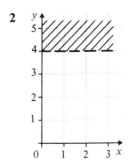

56

3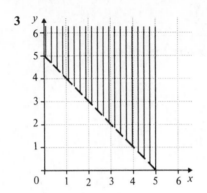

4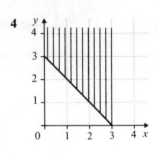

5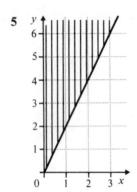

6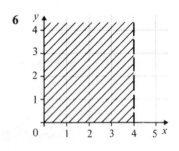

7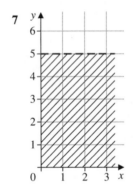

8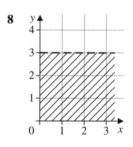

9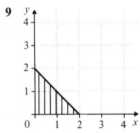

10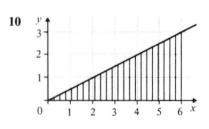

Illustrate the following regions.

11 $x > 5$	**12** $y > 3$	**13** $y \geqslant 6$	**14** $x + y \geqslant 6$	**15** $y \geqslant 3x$
16 $x < 2$	**17** $y < 7$	**18** $x + y < 4$	**19** $x \leqslant 3$	**20** $y \leqslant 5$

Unit 6 Representing solids

Using isometric paper

Isometric or triangular grids can help to draw two-dimensional (2-D) drawings of three-dimensional (3-D) objects.

Example 1

Draw this model made from cubes on isometric paper.

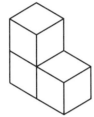

This is the drawing.

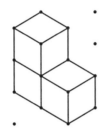

Exercise 6.1

Make each of these objects from cubes.
Then draw the objects on isometric paper.

1

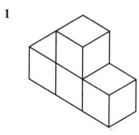

2

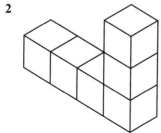

3

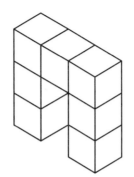

4

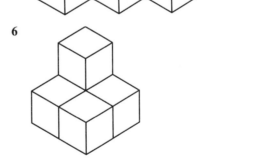

5

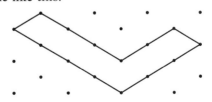

6

Example 2

Lenny cut some letters out of plywood and painted them. He put the letter L down on his desk when the paint was still wet and it left an outline like this.

Draw the letter on isometric paper.

58

The drawing looks like this.

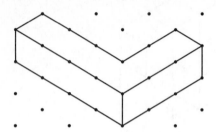

Exercise 6.2

Use isometric paper to draw the letters which left outlines like these on Lenny's desk.

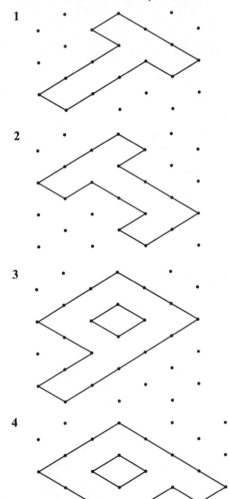

1

2

3

4

5

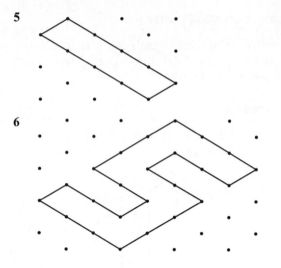

6

Example 3

This solid

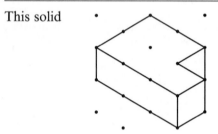

is resting on this base

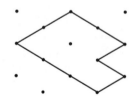

Draw the solid resting on this base

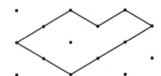

The drawing looks like this.

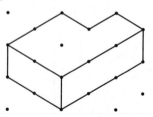

Exercise 6.3

1 Draw the solid resting on this base.

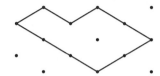

2 Draw the solid resting on this base.

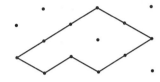

3 Draw this solid

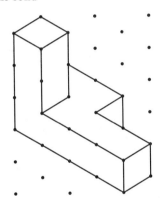

resting on this base

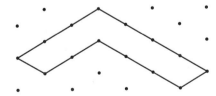

4 Draw this solid

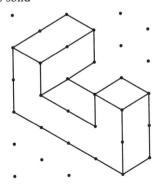

resting on this base

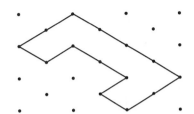

Exercise 6.4

Look at this set of 4 solids.

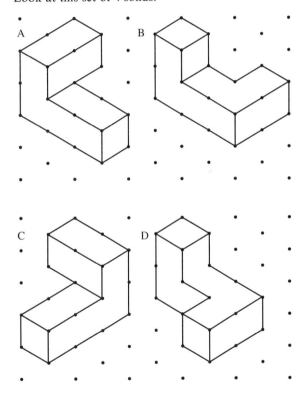

Now look at this set of 8 solids

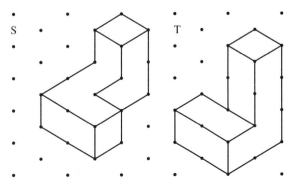

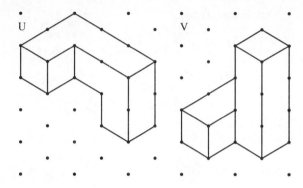

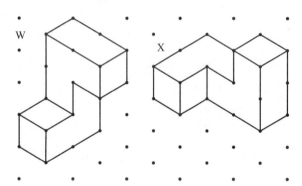

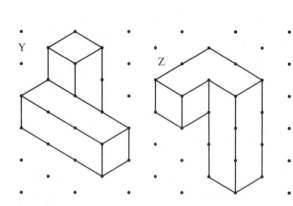

1 Which 2 of the 8 solids match Solid A?
2 Which 2 of the 8 solids match Solid B?
3 Which 2 of the 8 solids match Solid C?
4 Which 2 of the 8 solids match Solid D?

Exercise 6.5

This is a drawing of a model church made with wooden building bricks.

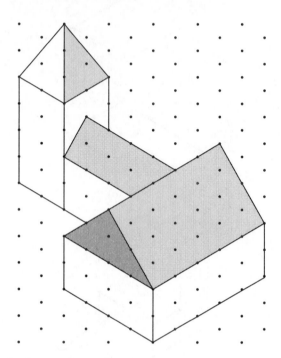

1 Copy and complete this drawing of the church from a different viewpoint.

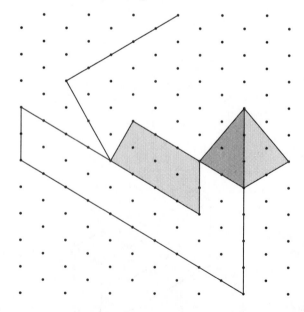

2 Draw your own model building on isometric paper.

Example 4

Here is one of Lenny's letters lying on a desk. 3 small creatures are looking at it.

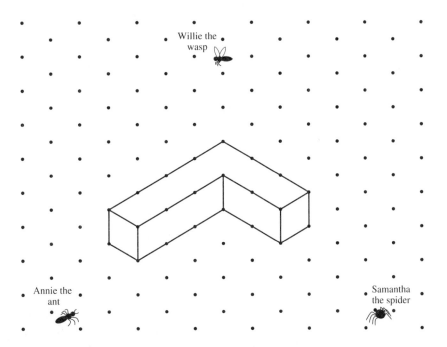

Here are three different views of the letter.

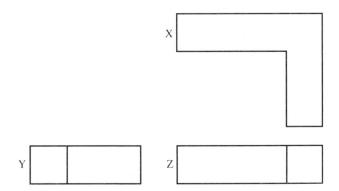

a Which is Annie's view of the letter?
b Which is Samantha's view of the letter?
c Which is Willie's view of the letter?

a Y is Annie's view of the letter.
b Z is Samantha's view of the letter.
c X is Willie's view of the letter.

Exercise 6.6

Draw Willie's, Annie's and Samantha's view of each of these letters.
Make each drawing like this.

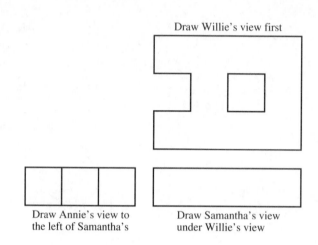

Draw Willie's view first

Draw Annie's view to
the left of Samantha's

Draw Samantha's view
under Willie's view

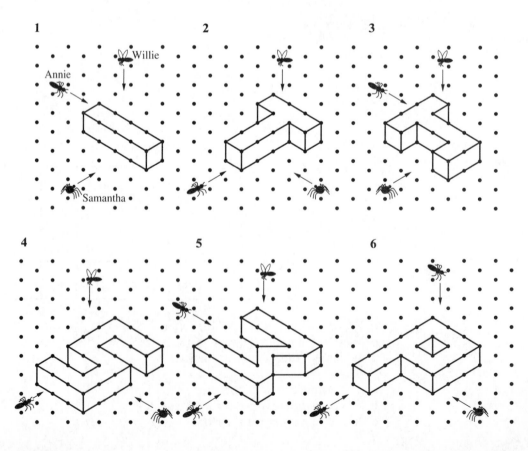

Plan and elevation

A view seen from directly above an object is called a *plan*.

A view seen from the front of an object is called a *front elevation*.

A view seen from the side of an object is called a *side elevation*.

Example 5

Draw a plan, front elevation and side elevation of this object.

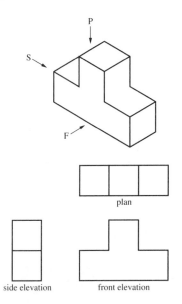

plan

side elevation   front elevation

Exercise 6.7

Draw a plan, front elevation and side elevation of each object.

1

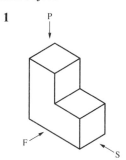

2

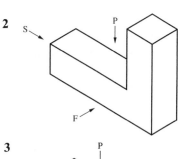

3

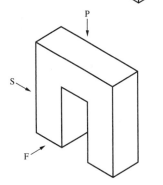

4

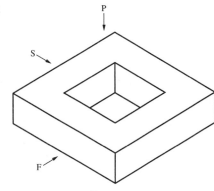

5

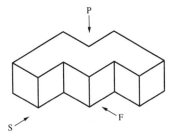

6

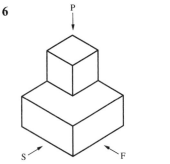

64

Exercise 6.8

These drawings show the plans, front elevations and side elevations of 6 objects.
Draw each object on isometric paper.

1

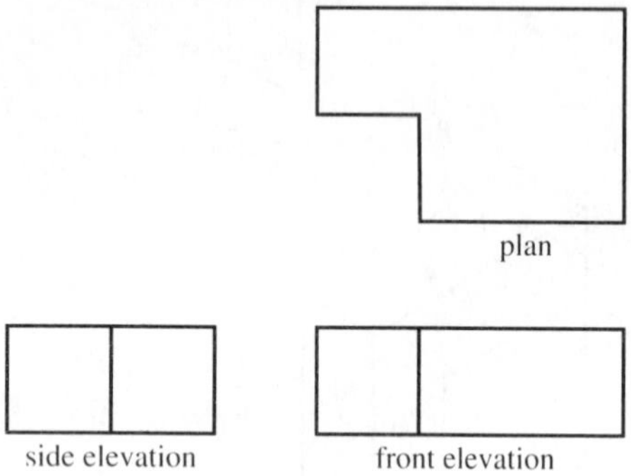

plan

side elevation   front elevation

2

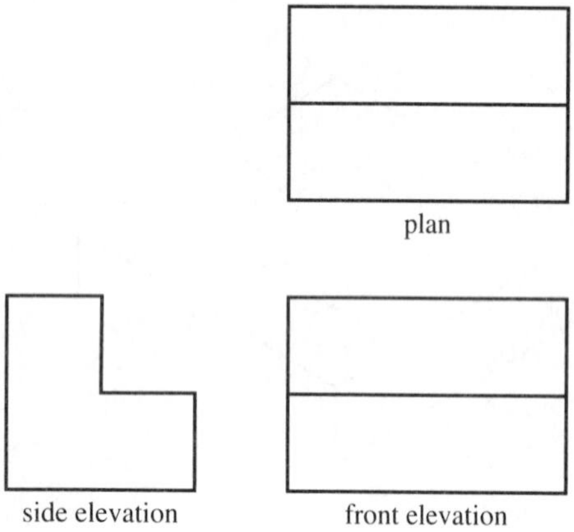

plan

side elevation   front elevation

3

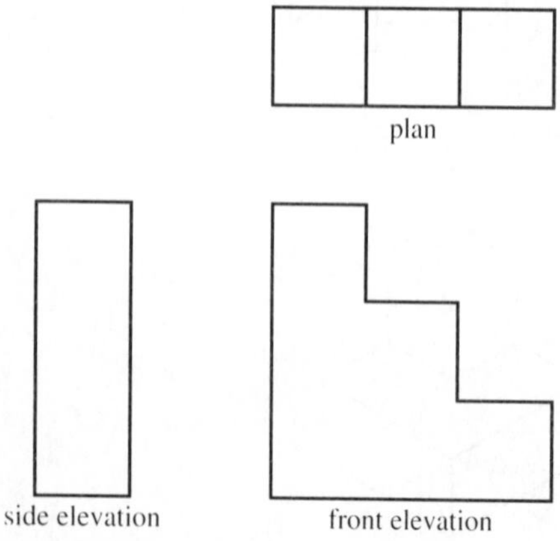

plan

side elevation   front elevation

4

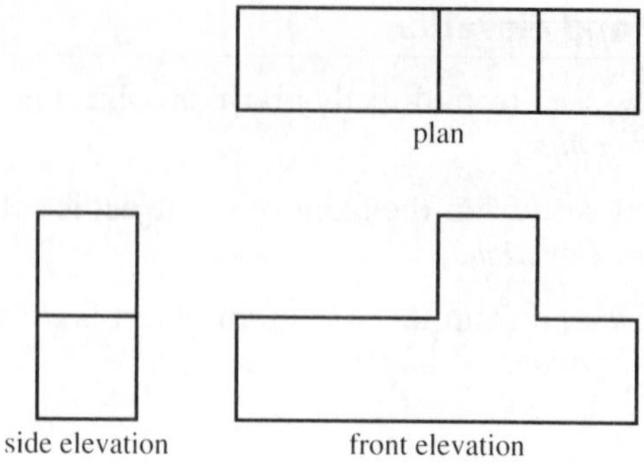

plan

side elevation   front elevation

5

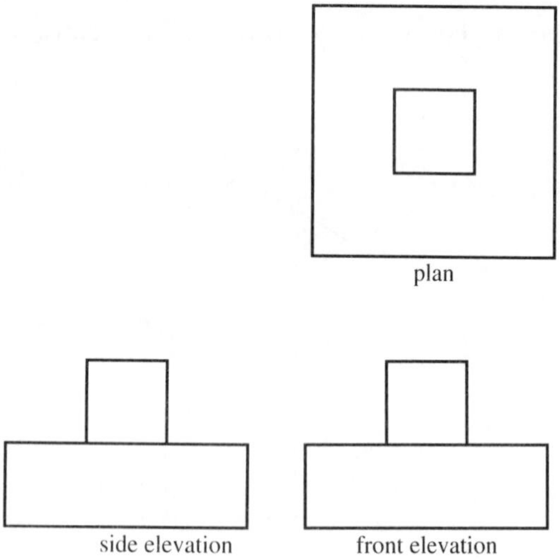

plan

side elevation   front elevation

6

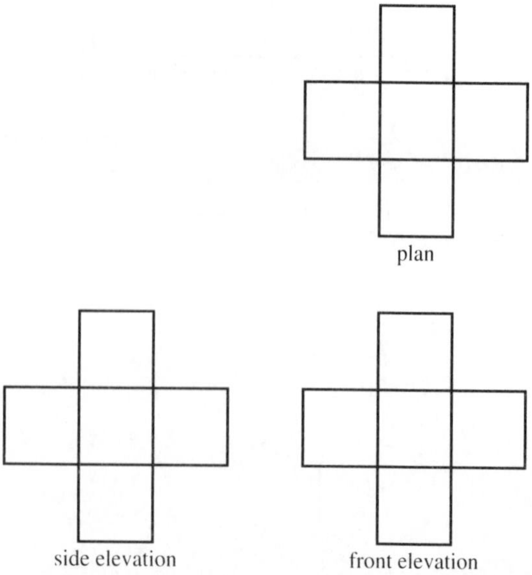

plan

side elevation   front elevation

Unit 7 Probability

Reminder
The probability of an event happening is

$$\frac{\text{number of outcomes which contain the event}}{\text{total number of outcomes}}$$

A probability can be written as a fraction, decimal or percentage. Decimal answers are easier to illustrate and compare on the probability scale from 0 (impossible) to 1 (certain). If decimal answers are very long they should be rounded to a sensible number of decimal places.

The probability scale

0	0.1	0.2	0.3	0.4	0.5	0.6	0.7	0.8	0.9	1

(impossible)   (certain)

Example 1

In a class of 24 girls, 12 wear dresses, 8 wear skirts and blouses and the rest wear jeans.

a Find the probability that the first girl to go into the classroom will be wearing
(i) a skirt and blouse   (ii) jeans

b Illustrate your answers on the probability scale.

a (i) number of outcomes which contain the event = 8
total number of outcomes = 24
So, the probability = $\frac{8}{24}$ or 0.33 (to 2 dp)
(ii) number of outcomes which contain the event = 4
total number of outcomes = 24
So, the probability = $\frac{4}{24}$ or 0.17 (to 2 dp)

b

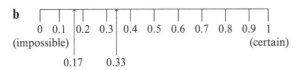

Exercise 7.1

In each question give your answers as fractions and decimals (correct to a sensible number of places). Illustrate all the answers to the question on a single probability scale.

1 There are 20 boys in class 5B; 12 of them have dark hair, 6 of them have blonde hair and 2 of them have ginger hair.
Find the probability that the first boy to go into the classroom will have
  a dark hair
  b blonde hair
  c ginger hair.

2 There are 30 players on a rugby pitch, 6 of them wear size ten boots, 15 of them wear size nine boots and 9 of them wear size eight boots.
Find the probability that the first player to leave the pitch at the end of the game will be wearing
  a size ten boots
  b size nine boots
  c size eight boots.

3 A teacher has a box of 36 coloured chalks, 6 of which are green, 12 of which are blue, 3 of which are yellow and 15 of which are red.
If he removes one stick at random, find the probability that it will be
  a green
  b blue
  c yellow
  d red.

4 There are 60 passengers on a bus, 30 are sitting downstairs, 24 are sitting upstairs and 6 are standing.
If the bus stops and one passenger gets off, find the probability that this passenger was
  a sitting downstairs
  b sitting upstairs
  c standing.

5 There are 360 passengers on a train, 240 are sitting in second-class seats, 90 are sitting in first-class seats and 30 are sitting in the buffet car.
If the train stops at a station, find the probability that the first passenger to get off was
  a sitting in a second-class seat
  b sitting in a first-class seat
  c sitting in the buffet car.

6 In a £1 cash bag there are 8 one penny coins, 6 two pence coins, 4 five pence coins and 6 ten pence coins.
If a coin is removed from the bag, find the probability that it will be
a a one penny coin   **b** a two pence coin
c a five pence coin   **d** a ten pence coin
e a copper coin   **f** a silver coin.

7 The dominoes illustrated below are shuffled and placed upside-down on a table.

If one is then picked up, find the probability that it will have
a 7 dots
b any odd number of dots
c any even number of dots.

8 The names of the four seasons of the year are written on cards.
If any one card is chosen at random, find the probability that
a the first letter on the card is S
b the last letter on the card is R
c there are six letters on the card.

9 For a geography quiz the names of 12 English cities are written on cards and the cards are then placed in a bag. The names are as follows

BIRMINGHAM   LIVERPOOL
BRISTOL   LONDON
BRADFORD   MANCHESTER
HULL   NEWCASTLE
LEEDS   NOTTINGHAM
LEICESTER   SHEFFIELD

If one card is removed from the bag, find the probability that
a the first letter on the card is B
b the first letter on the card is L
c the first letter on the card is N
d there are ten letters on the card
e there are nine letters on the card.

10 For a classroom game, the names of all 16 girls in class 3A are written on cards and the cards are then placed in a bag. The names are

ALISON   LESLEY   MARY   JILL
ANDREA   LINDA   MAVIS   JOANNE
ANGELA   MANDY   JANET   JUDITH
ANNE   MARION   JANICE   JUNE

If one card is removed from the bag find the probability that
a the first letter on the card is A
b the first letter on the card is L
c the first letter on the card is M
d the first letter on the card is J
e there are six letters on the card
f there are five letters on the card
g there are four letters on the card.

Relative frequency

Reminder

There are three ways to establish a probability.

1 By logical argument if we are certain that all outcomes are equally likely.
2 By using existing data, for example, school registers or weather records.
3 By conducting a survey or experiment.

Method 3 uses *relative frequency* as an estimate of probability. If the experiment or survey is only repeated a few times, the estimate will not be very accurate. To obtain an accurate estimate the experiment must be repeated a large number of times.

Example 2

Two pupils each select 100 seeds at random from a bag containing a very large number of red and white seeds. Each seed is returned to the bag before another is selected.

These are their results.

Carl	red	57
	white	43
Sherene	red	47
	white	53

a Write down the relative frequencies of red or white seeds for each pupil's results.
b Write down the relative frequencies of red or white seeds for the combined results.
c Which relative frequencies are likely to be the most accurate estimate of the probabilities that a selected seed is red or white?
d If there are 10 000 seeds in the bag, estimate the number of red seeds.

a The relative frequencies are:

Carl	red	$\frac{57}{100} = 0.57$
	white	$\frac{43}{100} = 0.43$
Sherene	red	$\frac{47}{100} = 0.47$
	white	$\frac{53}{100} = 0.53$

b The combined relative frequencies are

| | red | $\frac{104}{200} = 0.52$ |
| | white | $\frac{96}{200} = 0.48$ |

c The combined results are likely to be the most accurate.

d The best estimate will be

$$0.52 \times 10\,000 = 52\,000$$

Exercise 7.2

1 Five pupils each toss two coins twenty times. These are their results.

Nicola	two heads	6
	two tails	4
	heads and tails	10
Edward	two heads	4
	two tails	9
	heads and tails	7
Wayne	two heads	5
	two tails	4
	heads and tails	11
Clare	two heads	6
	two tails	2
	heads and tails	12
Madrina	two heads	2
	two tails	5
	heads and tails	13

a Write down the relative frequencies of two heads, two tails, or heads and tails for each pupil's results.
b Write down the relative frequencies of two heads, two tails, or heads and tails for the combined results.
c Which relative frequencies are likely to be the most accurate estimate of the probabilities that two tossed coins land as two heads, two tails or as heads and tails?

2 Four research students each open 25 pea pods and count the number of peas inside. These are their results.

Student A
number of peas	3	4	5	6	7	8
frequency	3	5	11	3	2	1

Student B
number of peas	3	4	5	6	7	8
frequency	4	5	6	7	3	0

Student C
number of peas	3	4	5	6	7	8
frequency	1	8	5	6	0	5

Student D
number of peas	3	4	5	6	7	8
frequency	2	4	7	8	4	0

a Write down the relative frequencies of 3, 4, 5, 6, 7 or 8 peas per pod for each student's results.

b Write down the relative frequencies of 3, 4, 5, 6, 7 or 8 peas per pod for the combined results.

c Which relative frequencies are likely to be the most accurate estimate of the probabilities that a pod contains 3, 4, 5, 6, 7 or 8 peas?

d In a sample of 1000 pods, how many would you expect to contain 5 peas?

e In a sample of 2000 pods, how many would you expect to contain fewer than 5 peas?

3 Five Trading Standards Officers each open 20 boxes of Striko Matches and count the contents. These are their results.

Officer A

number of matches	38	39	40	41	42
number of boxes	2	6	7	5	0

Officer B

number of matches	38	39	40	41	42
number of boxes	1	5	8	5	1

Officer C

number of matches	38	39	40	41	42
number of boxes	0	4	12	4	0

Officer D

number of matches	38	39	40	41	42
number of boxes	3	4	5	7	1

Officer E

number of matches	38	39	40	41	42
number of boxes	1	8	10	0	1

a Write down the relative frequencies of 38, 39, 40, 41 or 42 matches per box for each officer's results.

b Write down the relative frequencies of 38, 39, 40, 41 or 42 matches per box for the combined results.

c Which relative frequencies are likely to be the most accurate estimate of the probabilities that a box contains 38, 39, 40, 41 or 42 matches?

d In a survey of 1000 boxes, how many would you expect to contain 40 matches?

e In a survey of 2000 boxes, how many would you expect to contain more than 40 matches?

4 In an experiment, 4 groups of 50 people are asked to select their favourite colour from red, blue, green and yellow. These are the results.

Group A

colour	R	B	G	Y
number	21	12	7	10

Group B

colour	R	B	G	Y
number	17	18	5	10

Group C

colour	R	B	G	Y
number	28	13	7	7

Group D

colour	R	B	G	Y
number	20	16	11	3

a Write down the relative frequencies of red, blue, green and yellow for each group's results.

b Write down the relative frequencies of red, blue, green and yellow for the combined results.

c Which relative frequencies are likely to be the most accurate estimate of the probabilities that a person selects red, blue, green or yellow as their favourite colour?

d If 1500 people are asked to select their favourite colour from red, blue, green and yellow, how many would you expect to select red?

e If 5000 people are asked to select their favourite colour from red, blue, green and yellow, how many would you expect to select a colour other than red?

Identifying outcomes

Two coins are tossed.

a What is the probability that the result is two heads?

b If the two coins are tossed 1000 times, how many of the results would you predict will be two heads?

When we are dealing with two events, a table like a graph helps to identify all the possible outcomes. This is a table for two coins.

T	HT	TT
H	HH	TH
	H	T

second coin

first coin

a The table shows us there are 4 possible results: Heads Heads, Heads Tails, Tails Heads and Tails Tails. Therefore the probability of the result Heads Heads is $\frac{1}{4}$ or 0.25.

b In 1000 throws we would predict $1000 \times 0.25 = 250$ heads

Example 3

Two fair spinners are made, one numbered 1, 2 and 3 and the other numbered 1, 2, 3, 4.

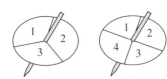

A total score is obtained by spinning the spinners and adding the two scores.

a Draw a table identifying all the possible results when the two spinners are spun.
b What is the probability that the total score is greater than 5?
c What is the probability of a score of 3?
d If the spinners are spun 100 times, how many of the results would you predict will be scores of 3?

a This table identifies all the possible results.

second spinner

4	5	6	7
3	4	5	6
2	3	4	5
1	2	3	4
	1	2	3

first spinner

b The probability that the total score is greater than 5 is $\frac{3}{12}$ or 0.25.

c The probability that the total score is 3 is $\frac{2}{12}$ or 0.17 (to 2 decimal places).

d In 100 throws we would predict $100 \times 0.17 = 17$ scores of 3.

Exercise 7.3

1 If two coins are tossed 2000 times, how many of the results would you predict will be
   a two heads
   b two tails
   c one head and one tail?

2 Two fair spinners are made, one numbered 1, 2, 3 and the other numbered 1, 2, 3, 4, 5.

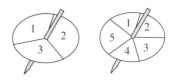

A total score is obtained by spinning the spinners and adding the two scores.
   a Draw a table identifying all the possible results when the two spinners are spun.
   b What is the probability that the total score is greater than 5?
   c What is the probability that the total score is 5?

3 Two fair spinners are made, one numbered 1, 3, 5 and the other numbered 2, 4, 6.

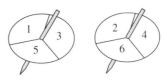

A total score is obtained by spinning the spinners and adding the two scores.
   a Draw a table identifying all the possible results when the two spinners are spun.
   b What is the probability that the total score is greater than 5?
   c What is the probability that the total score is 5?

4 Two fair spinners are made, one numbered 1, 2, 3 and the other numbered 1, 2, 3, 4.

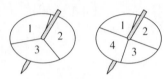

A total score is obtained by spinning the spinners and multiplying the two scores.
a Draw a table identifying all the possible results when the two spinners are spun.
b What is the probability that the total score is greater than 4?
c What is the probability that the total score is an even number?
d If the two spinners are spun 1200 times, how many of the results would you predict will be
(i) 2   (ii) 9?

5 Two fair spinners are made, one numbered 1, 2, 3 and the other numbered 1, 2, 3, 4, 5.

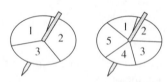

A total score is obtained by spinning the spinners and multiplying the two scores.
a Draw a table identifying all the possible results when the two spinners are spun.
b What is the probability that the total score is
(i) 1   (ii) 2   (iii) 3   (iv) 4   (v) 5
(vi) 6   (vii) 8   (viii) 9   (ix) 10   (x) 15?
c If the two spinners are spun 1000 times, how many of the results would you predict will be
(i) 2   (ii) 15?

6 Two fair dice each numbered from 1 to 6 are rolled. The total score is obtained by adding the scores on the two dice.

a Draw a table identifying all the possible results when the two dice are rolled.

b What is the probability that the total score is
(i) 1   (ii) 2   (iii) 3   (iv) 4
(v) 5   (vi) 6   (vii) 7   (viii) 8
(ix) 9   (x) 10   (xi) 11   (xii) 12
(xiii) an odd number
(xiv) a factor of 12
(xv) greater than 5?
c If the two dice are rolled 3600 times, how many of the results would you predict will be
(i) 2   (ii) 7?

7 A pack of cards is cut twice and the suits (hearts, diamonds, spades or clubs) of the cards are noted

a Draw a table identifying all the possible results when the two suits are noted.
b What is the probability that the suits noted will be
(i) two hearts   (ii) one heart and one club
(iii) one black and one red card
(iv) a pair which contains one diamond
(v) a pair which contains at least one heart?
c If the experiment is repeated 1600 times, how many of the results would you predict will not contain a club?

8 Two special dice are made, one numbered 0, 0, 1, 1, 2, 2 and the other numbered 0, 0, 0, 1, 2, 3. William rolls the first dice and Mary rolls the second dice.

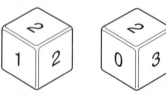

a Draw a table identifying all the possible results when William and Mary roll the dice.
Use the code W if William wins, M if Mary wins and D if it is a draw.
b They roll their dice 360 times each. How many times do you predict that William will beat Mary?

Tree diagrams

Tree diagrams are an alternative way of identifying all the outcomes when we are dealing with two events.

If two coins are tossed, the possible results can be illustrated on this tree diagram, as shown below.

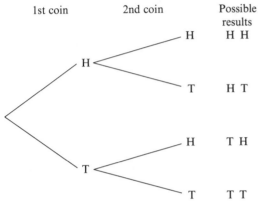

Questions on probability can be answered from this diagram.

e.g. probability of 2 heads = $\frac{1}{4}$ or 0.25.

Example 4

A box contains a red pen, a blue pen and a green pen. A pen is taken out, used, put back and a second pen taken out.
Draw a tree diagram to show all the possible results and from the diagram find
a the probability that both pens are red
b the probability that both pens are different colours.

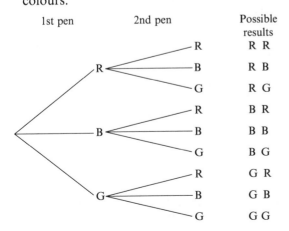

a total number of possibilities = 9
total number where are both red = 1
So, the probability that both pens are red is $\frac{1}{9}$ or 0.11 (to 2 dp)

b total number of possibilities = 9
total number which involve different colours = 6
So, the probability that the two pens are of different colour is $\frac{6}{9}$ or 0.67 (to 2 dp).

Exercise 7.4

1 In my wallet there is a £5 note, a £10 note and a £20 note.
If I remove a note, put it back and then remove a note again, draw a tree diagram to show all the possible results.
From the diagram find
a the probability that both notes are the same
b the probability that the two notes are different
c the probability that both are £5 notes
d the probability that both are £10 notes
e the probability that both are £20 notes.

2 In my wallet there is a 10 p stamp, a 12 p stamp and a 20 p stamp.
If I remove a stamp, put it back and then remove a stamp again, draw a tree diagram to show all the possible results.
From the diagram find
a the probability that both stamps are the same
b the probability that the two stamps are different
c the probability that both stamps are worth more than 10 p.

3 In my pocket I have a 2 p coin, a 5 p coin and a 10 p coin.
If I remove a coin, put it back and then remove a coin again, draw a tree diagram to show all the possible results.
From the diagram find
a the probability that both coins are the same
b the probability that both coins are silver
c the probability that one coin is silver and the other is copper
d the probability that both coins are copper.

4 Three counters marked 1, 2 and 3 are placed in a bag.
If a counter is removed from the bag, replaced and then a counter is removed again, draw a tree diagram to show all the possible results.

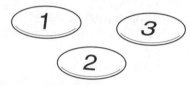

From the diagram find
a the probability that both counters are the same
b the probability that both counters are marked with odd numbers
c the probability that both counters are marked with even numbers.

5 Three counters marked 1, 4 and 6 are placed in a bag.
If a counter is removed from the bag, replaced and then a counter is removed again, draw a tree diagram to show all the possible results.
From the diagram find
a the probability that both counters are marked with odd numbers
b the probability that both counters are marked with even numbers
c the probability that both counters are marked with square numbers
d the probability that both counters are marked with triangular numbers.

6 Three counters marked A, B and C are placed in a bag.
If a counter is removed from the bag, replaced and then a counter is removed again, draw a tree diagram to show all the possible results.
From the diagram find
a the probability that both counters are marked with consonant letters
b the probability that both counters are marked with vowel letters
c the probability that one counter is marked with a consonant and the other with a vowel.

7 The three dominoes illustrated are placed upside-down on a table.

If one is picked up, replaced and then a domino is removed again, draw a tree diagram to show all the possible results.

From the diagram find
a the probability that both dominoes have the same number of dots
b the probability that both dominoes have six dots
c the probability that both dominoes have nine dots.

8 Three playing cards, the three of diamonds, the six of hearts and the six of clubs are placed upside-down on a table.
If one is picked up, replaced and then a card is removed again, draw a tree diagram to show all the possible results.
From the diagram find
a the probability that both cards are of the same number
b the probability that both cards are of a red suit
c the probability that both cards have a triangular number printed on them.

9 Three playing cards, the four of hearts, the six of clubs and the nine of spades are placed upside-down on a table.
If one is picked up, replaced and then a card is removed again, draw a tree diagram to show all the possible results.

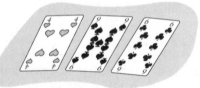

From the diagram find
a the probability that both cards are of a black suit
b the probability that both cards have square numbers printed on them.

10 Four counters marked 1, 2, 3, and 4 are placed in a bag.
If a counter is removed from the bag, replaced and then a counter is removed again, draw a tree diagram to show all the possible results.
From the diagram
a the probability that both counters are marked with odd numbers
b the probability that both counters are marked with even numbers
c the probability that both counters show numbers which are multiples of 2
d the probability that both counters show numbers which are factors of 6
e the probability that both counters show numbers which are factors of 12.

Example 5

I have two 20 p pieces and one 5 p piece in my pocket.
If I pick out two coins, find by drawing a tree diagram the probability that I obtain

a two 20 p coins
b one 20 p coin and one 5 p coin
c enough money to buy a 25 p stamp

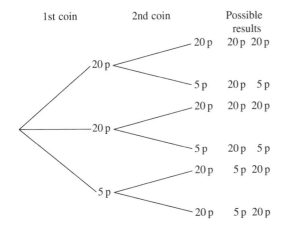

a probability of two 20 p coins = $\frac{2}{6}$ or 0.33 (to 2 dp)

b probability of one of each = $\frac{4}{6}$ or 0.67 (to 2 dp)

c Because any draw produces coins of the value of 25 p or more, then the probability is a certainty, or simply 1.

Exercise 7.5

1 I have two £5 notes and one £10 note in my wallet.
If I pick out two notes, find by drawing a tree diagram the probability that I obtain
a two £5 notes
b one note of each kind
c enough money to buy a rail ticket to London if the fare is £15.

2 I have three pieces of string in my pocket; their lengths are 50 cm, 50 cm and 80 cm.
If I pick out two of them, find by drawing a tree diagram the probability that I obtain
a two pieces which are of the same length
b two pieces which are of different lengths
c enough string for tying up a parcel which requires a total length of 120 cm.

3 I have two 50 p pieces and one 10 p piece in my pocket.
If I pick out two coins, find by drawing a tree diagram the probability that I obtain
a two 50 p coins
b one coin of each kind
c enough money to pay my bus fare home if it is 60 p.

4 I have a 2 p stamp, a 10 p stamp and a 15 p stamp in my wallet.
If I pick out two stamps, find by drawing a tree diagram the probability that I obtain
a two stamps which could be used for a letter which costs 25 p to post
b two stamps which can each be bought with a single coin.

5 I have a 20 p piece, a 10 p piece and a 2 p piece in my pocket.
If I pick out two coins, find by drawing a tree diagram the probability that I obtain
a two silver coins
b enough money to buy a 20 p stamp.

6 In my pocket I have three keys, one for the door of my house, one for my car door and one which is the car ignition key.
If I pick out two keys, find by drawing a tree diagram the probability that I obtain
a two keys which enable me to get into my car and start it
b two keys which enable me to lock up my house and get into my car.

7 The letters of the word SIT are printed on three counters and the counters are placed in a bag.

If I remove two counters from the bag, find by drawing a tree diagram the probability that I obtain
a two letters which are both consonants
b two letters which can be used to spell a word.

8 The letters of the word SINK are printed on four counters and the counters are placed in a bag.
If I remove two counters from the bag, find by drawing a tree diagram the probability that I obtain
   a two letters which are both consonants
   b two letters which can be used to spell a word.

9 The numbers 1, 3, 4 and 9 are printed on counters and the counters are placed in a bag.
If I remove two counters from the bag, find by drawing a tree diagram the probability that I obtain
   a two square numbers
   b two triangular numbers
   c two multiples of 3
   d two factors of 12.

10 Four playing cards, the five of diamonds, the nine of hearts, the nine of clubs and the nine of spades are placed upside-down on a table.
If I pick up two cards, find by drawing a tree diagram the probability that I obtain
   a two cards of the same number
   b two cards which are both of a red suit
   c two cards which are both of a black suit.

Plotting points

The axes of a graph may be drawn on both sides of the origin. The paper is then divided into four parts called *quadrants*.

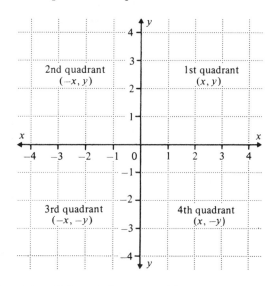

Distances to the right of the origin are positive.
Distances to the left of the origin are negative.
Distances upwards from the origin are positive.
Distances downwards from the origin are negative.

So both positive and negative values of x and y may be plotted. The ordered pair (x, y) which gives the position of any point is called its Cartesian coordinate.

Example 1

Write down the coordinates of the points shown on the following graph.

A is the point $(2, 1)$
B is the point $(-3, 2)$
C is the point $(-1, -4)$
D is the point $(2, -2)$

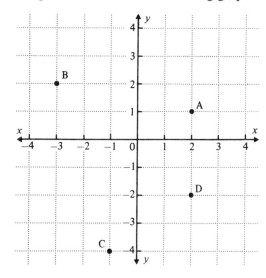

Exercise 8.1

Write down the coordinates of the points shown on the following graph.

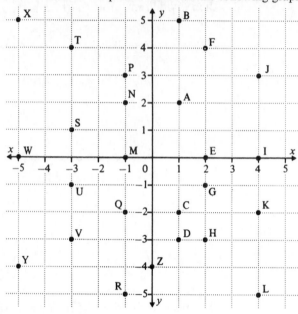

Example 2

Plot the following points and join each point to the next with a straight line. Suggest a name for the picture you have drawn.

$(2, -1), (2, -5), (3, -4),$
$(5, -4), (4, -5), (-3, -5),$
$(-1, -4), (-1, -2), (-3, 0),$
$(-2, 1), (-4, 3), (-4, 6),$
$(-2, 5), (0, 6), (0, 3),$
$(-1, 2), (2, -1).$

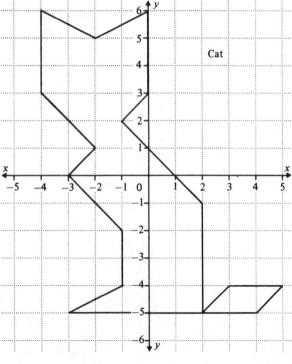

Exercise 8.2

On graph paper draw an x-axis numbered from -5 to 5 and a y-axis numbered from -10 to 10.
Plot the positions of the points in each question on your axes.
Join each point to the next with a straight line.
Then suggest a name for the picture you have drawn.

1 (1, 10), (1, 5), (2, 4), (2, −5), (1, −6), (0, −6), (−1, −5), (−1, 4), (0, 5), (0, 10), (1, 10).

2 (0, 10), (4, −1), (1, −1), (1, −2), (2, −2), (1, −6), (−1, −6), (−2, −2), (−1, −2), (−1, −1), (−4, −1), (0, 10).

3 (3, 10), (4, 9), (4, 7), (3, 6), (5, 6), (5, −6), (3, −6), (4, −7), (4, −9), (3, −10), (2, −9), (2, −7), (3, −6), (1, −6), (1, 6), (3, 6), (2, 7), (2, 9), (3, 10).

4 (0, 9), (3, 4), (1, 4), (1, −4), (3, −6), (3, −7), (1, −5), (1, −6), (3, −8), (3, −9), (1, −7), (1, −9), (−1, −9), (−1, −7), (−3, −9), (−3, −8), (−1, −6), (−1, −5), (−3, −7), (−3, −6), (−1, −4), (−1, 4), (−3, 4), (0, 9).

5 (1, 10), (1, −1), (2, 9), (3, 10), (4, 9), (4, −7), (3, −10), (3, −5), (4, −5), (3, −5), (3, 9), (2, −1), (2, −3), (−1, −3), (1, −3), (1, −7), (−1, −7), (1, −7), (0, −10), (−1, −7), (−1, −3), (−2, −3), (−2, −1), (1, −1), (−1, −1), (−1, 10), (1, 10).

For questions 6 to 11, draw both the x-axis and the y-axis numbered from -12 to 12.

6 (4, 5), (4, 3), (5, 4), (6, 3), (6, 1), (5, 0), (4, 1), (4, −2), (3, −3), (7, −2), (7, −3), (3, −4), (−3, −4), (−7, −3), (−7, −2), (−3, −3), (3, −3), (−3, −3), (−4, −2), (−4, 5), (4, 5).

7 (2, 4), (3, 5), (7, 5), (8, 1), (9, 1), (10, −1), (9, −3), (7, −5), (−1, −5), (−6, −4), (−7, 0), (−4, 1), (8, 1), (3, 1), (2, 2), (2, 3), (−10, 4), (2, 4).

8 (2, 5), (4, 5), (6, 4), (7, 1), (7, −4), (6, −5), (5, −5), (6, −4), (6, 0), (5, −1), (4, 0), (2, 2), (4, 4), (5, 2), (5, 3), (6, 3), (6, 2), (5, 2), (5, 1), (4, 0), (4, −5), (5, −6), (2, −6), (2, −1), (−5, −1), (−6, −2), (−6, −5), (−5, −6), (−7, −6), (−8, −1), (−8, 1), (−7, 3), (−3, 4), (0, 4), (2, 5).

9 (8, 4), (9, 3), (10, 3), (11, 2), (11, −4), (10, −6), (9, −6), (10, −4), (10, 2), (9, 2), (9, 0), (8, −1), (9, −4), (8, −9), (7, −9), (8, −4), (6, −2), (7, −4), (6, −9), (5, −9), (6, −4), (5, −2), (−1, −2), (−1, −8), (−2, −9), (−3, −9), (−2, −8), (−2, −3), (−3, 0), (−3, −8), (−4, −9), (−5, −9), (−4, −8), (−4, 0), (−7, 5), (−8, 5), (−10, 3), (−11, 3), (−12, 4), (−12, 5), (−10, 7), (−10, 6), (−9, 6), (−10, 7), (−9, 8), (−9, 9), (−8, 8), (−7, 8), (−1, 4), (8, 4).

10 (2, 4), (0, 6), (4, 10), (6, 8), (0, 2), (2, 0), (2, 4), (2, 0), (4, 2), (8, −2), (6, −4), (2, 0), (2, −4), (3, −10), (−3, −10), (−2, −4), (0, −2), (−2, 0), (0, −2), (−4, −6), (−6, −4), (0, 2), (−2, 4), (−2, 0), (−2, 4), (−4, 2), (−8, 6), (−6, 8), (−2, 4), (−2, 6), (−1, 7), (1, 7).

11 (−9, −12), (−9, 11), (−10, 12), (−6, 12), (−7, 11), (−7, 10), (−6, 9), (−6, −3), (−6, 9), (2, 9), (2, 4), (−6, 4), (2, 4), (2, 9), (4, 9), (4, 4), (12, 4), (4, 4), (4, 9), (12, 9), (12, −3), (4, −3), (4, 2), (12, 2), (4, 2), (4, −3), (2, −3), (2, 2), (−6, 2), (2, 2), (2, −3), (−6, −3), (−7, −4), (−7, 10), (−7, −12).

Straight line graphs

Example 3

The graph below shows the line

$$y = 2x + 1$$

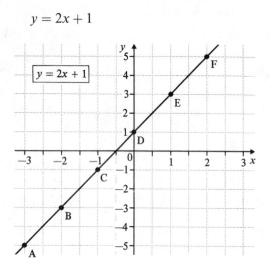

The table is for the coordinates of all the lettered points which lie on the line $y = 2x + 1$.

	A	B	C	D	E	F
x	−3			0		
y	−5			1		

Copy and complete the table by filling in the missing values of x and y. The points A and D are already done for you. The coordinates of A are $(−3, −5)$, and those of D are $(0, 1)$.

From the graph
  point B is $(−2, −3)$
  point C is $(−1, −1)$
  point E is $(1, 3)$
  point F is $(2, 5)$

The completed table then looks like this

	A	B	C	D	E	F
x	−3	−2	−1	0	1	2
y	−5	−3	−1	1	3	5

Exercise 8.3

For each graph, copy and complete the table of values, giving the coordinates of the lettered points which lie on the line.

1 $y = 2x − 3$

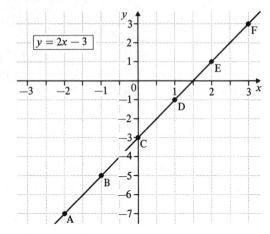

	A	B	C	D	E	F
x	−2			0	1	
y	−7			−3	−1	

2 $y = 2x + 4$

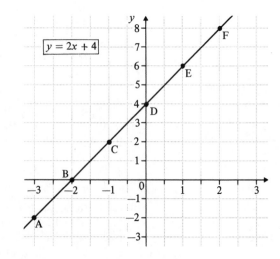

	A	B	C	D	E	F
x		−2	−1	0		
y		0	2	4		

3 $y = 2x - 4$

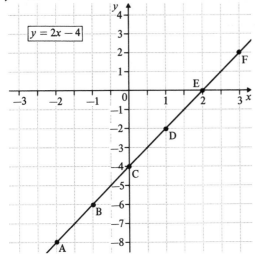

	A	B	C	D	E	F
x					2	
y					0	

4 $y = 3x + 1$

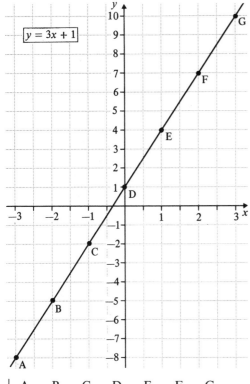

	A	B	C	D	E	F	G
x							
y							

Example 4

The table of values gives the coordinates of points that lie on the line $y = 1 - x$.

x	-3	-2	-1	0	1	2	3
y	4	3	2	1	0	-1	-2

Plot the line $y = 1 - x$ from these values.

Your completed graph should look like this.

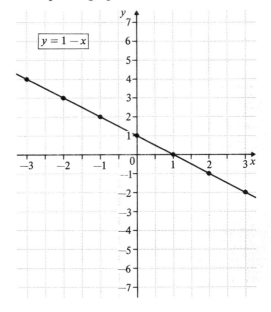

Exercise 8.4

For each question plot the graph of the equation on squared paper from the table of values given.

1 $y = x + 4$

x	-3	-2	-1	0	1	2	3
y	1	2	3	4	5	6	7

2 $y = x + 3$

x	-3	-2	-1	0	1	2	3
y	0	1	2	3	4	5	6

3 $y = x + 1$

x	-3	-2	-1	0	1	2	3
y	-2	-1	0	1	2	3	4

4 $y = x - 2$

x	-3	-2	-1	0	1	2	3
y	-5	-4	-3	-2	-1	0	1

5 $y = x - 4$

x	-3	-2	-1	0	1	2	3
y	-7	-6	-5	-4	-3	-2	-1

6 $y = x - 3$

x	-3	-2	-1	0	1	2	3
y	-6	-5	-4	-3	-2	-1	0

7 $y = 4 - x$

x	-3	-2	-1	0	1	2	3
y	7	6	5	4	3	2	1

8 $y = 2 - x$

x	-3	-2	-1	0	1	2	3
y	5	4	3	2	1	0	-1

9 $y = 3 - x$

x	-3	-2	-1	0	1	2	3
y	6	5	4	3	2	1	0

10 $y = -x$

x	-3	-2	-1	0	1	2	3
y	3	2	1	0	-1	-2	-3

A table of values must first be made out before the graph of an equation can be plotted.

Example 5

Make out a table of values for the equation $y = 2x + 1$ from $x = -2$ to $x = 2$.

values of x	-2	-1	0	1	2
$2x$	-4	-2	0	2	4
$+1$	$+1$	$+1$	$+1$	$+1$	$+1$
values of y	-3	-1	$+1$	$+3$	$+5$

The first value of y is found as follows.

When $x = -2$, $2x = 2 \times -2 = -4$

so $y = 2x + 1 = -4 + 1 = -3$

Exercise 8.5

Copy and complete each table of values.

1 $y = 2x + 5$

x	-2	-1	0	1	2
$2x$					
$+5$					
y					

2 $y = 2x + 8$

x	-2	-1	0	1	2
$2x$					
$+8$					
y					

3 $y = 4x + 3$

x	-2	-1	0	1	2
$4x$					
$+3$					
y					

4 $y = 4x + 1$

x	-2	-1	0	1	2
$4x$					
$+1$					
y					

5 $y = 4x - 1$

x	-2	-1	0	1	2
$4x$					
-1					
y					

6 $y = 4x - 3$

x	-2	-1	0	1	2
$4x$					
-3					
y					

7 $y = 5x + 2$

x	-2	-1	0	1	2
$5x$					
$+2$					
y					

Example 6

Draw the graph of $y = 3x - 2$ for values of x from -2 to $+2$.
Use a scale of 1 cm to 1 unit on the x-axis and a scale of 1 cm to 2 units on the y-axis.

Step 1
Produce a table of values as follows.

x	-2	-1	0	1	2
$3x$	-6	-3	0	3	6
-2	-2	-2	-2	-2	-2
y	-8	-5	-2	1	4

Step 2
Draw the axes, plot the points and then join up the points on the graph with a straight line.

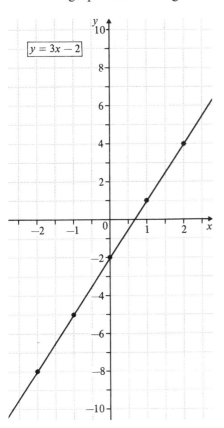

Exercise 8.6

For questions **1** to **5**, copy and complete the table, then plot the graph of the equation given.
Use a scale of 1 cm to 1 unit on the x-axis and a scale of 1 cm to 2 units on the y-axis.

1 $y = 2x - 2$

x	-2	-1	0	1	2
$2x$					
-2					
y					

2 $y = 3x - 1$

x	-2	-1	0	1	2
$3x$					
-1					
y					

3 $y = x - 1$

x	-2	-1	0	1	2
x					
-1					
y					

4 $y = x + 2$

x	-2	-1	0	1	2
x					
$+2$					
y					

5 $y = 2x + 3$

x	-2	-1	0	1	2
$2x$					
$+3$					
y					

For questions **6** to **15**, draw up a table of values from $x = -2$ to $x = +2$ for the given equation. Then plot the graph of the equation. Use a scale of 1 cm to 1 unit on the x-axis and a scale of 1 cm to 2 units on the y-axis.

6 $y = 3x + 2$ **7** $y = 3x + 4$
8 $y = 2x + 2$ **9** $y = 2x$
10 $y = 2x - 1$ **11** $y = 3x - 3$
12 $y = 3x - 1$ **13** $y = 4x$
14 $y = 4x - 2$ **15** $y = 5x$

Unit 9 Correlation

If two variables are *correlated*, this means that they are linked in some way.

If, as the value of one variable increases, the value of the other variable also tends to increase the variables are *positively correlated*.
If, as the value of one variable increases, the value of the other variable tends to decrease the variables are *negatively correlated*.

For example, we might say, 'Tall people tend to be heavier than shorter people'.
This statement is equivalent to saying, 'In humans, height and weight are positively correlated'.

Or we might say, 'As new cars age, their value falls'.
This statement is equivalent to saying, 'In new cars, age and value are negatively correlated'.

A *scatter diagram* can be used to test if two variables are correlated.

Example 1

These are the test scores for 10 pupils in Maths and Science.

person	A	B	C	D	E	F	G	H	I	J
maths score	9	3	6	7	4	5	1	6	8	9
science score	8	4	5	6	5	4	2	7	8	10

a Draw a scatter diagram.
b Comment on any correlation indicated in the scatter diagram.

a This is the scatter diagram, with each person's pair of scores represented by a point.
For example, person A scored 9 and 8 and this is represented by the point (9, 8).

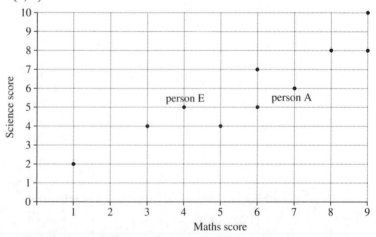

b The scatter diagram indicates there is a positive correlation between Maths and Science marks. This means that pupils who score a high mark for Maths tend to also score a high mark for Science. Pupils who score a low mark for Maths tend to also score a low mark for Science.

Example 2

These are the ages of 10 children and their times to run 100 m.

child	A	B	C	D	E	F	G	H	I	J
age	8	4	11	8	6	7	5	4	9	10
time (seconds)	17	23	14	15	20	20	22	26	15	16

a Draw a scatter diagram.

b Comment on any correlation indicated in the scatter diagram.

a

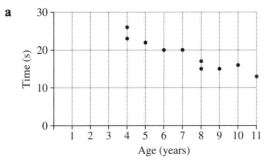

b The scatter diagram indicates there is a negative correlation between age and the time taken to run 100 m. This means that as the age *increases* the time taken to run 100 m tends to *decrease*.

If the dots in a scatter diagram are distributed at random, this indicates there is no correlation between the variables.

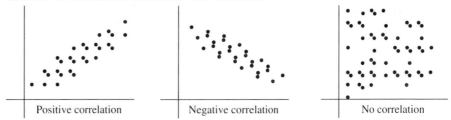

| Positive correlation | Negative correlation | No correlation |

Exercise 9.1

1 This table records the Year Group of 20 students and their number of days absent from school in the year.

pupil	A	B	C	D	E	F	G	H	I	J
year	7	8	7	9	11	10	7	8	10	11
days absent	0	5	3	5	15	15	5	0	5	20

pupil	K	L	M	N	O	P	Q	R	S	T
year	7	8	9	9	9	11	11	10	10	8
days absent	10	7	8	10	12	10	12	10	13	10

a Draw a scatter diagram.

b Comment on any correlation indicated in the scatter diagram.

2 This table records the temperature each day in June and the number of ice-creams a shopkeeper sells.

date	1st	2nd	3rd	4th	5th	6th	7th	8th	9th	10th
temperature	20	19	19	18	16	14	15	17	16	14
number sold	21	20	22	17	14	10	16	18	15	13

date	11th	12th	13th	14th	15th	16th	17th	18th	19th	20th
temperature	16	18	20	21	22	24	27	29	27	26
number sold	14	18	22	14	14	27	27	32	18	25

date	21st	22nd	23rd	24th	25th	26th	27th	28th	29th	30th
temperature	24	26	22	21	17	18	19	16	12	9
number sold	26	27	22	22	16	16	19	12	11	12

a Draw a scatter diagram.
b Comment on any correlation indicated in the scatter diagram.

3 The length of 20 girls' hair (measured in inches) and their shoe size is recorded in this table.

girl	A	B	C	D	E	F	G	H	I	J
hair length	5	6	12	8	8	9	12	6	7	8
shoe size	4	3	4	5	7	2	5	4	5	3

girl	K	L	M	N	O	P	Q	R	S	T
hair length	15	6	7	5	2	9	10	11	7	12
shoe size	4	8	5	7	7	5	3	4	7	3

a Draw a scatter diagram.
b Comment on any correlation indicated in the scatter diagram.

4 A Security Firm experiments with the number of guards it deploys each night on a large industrial estate. This table records the number of guards deployed during 20 different months and the number of reported thefts.

month	1	2	3	4	5	6	7	8	9	10
number of guards	4	3	2	4	5	7	6	8	10	12
number of thefts	15	20	23	17	13	12	10	9	7	5

month	11	12	13	14	15	16	17	18	19	20
number of guards	15	14	12	10	8	7	6	4	4	8
number of thefts	3	4	6	8	10	11	12	16	13	8

a Draw a scatter diagram.
b Comment on any correlation indicated in the scatter diagram.

5 This table records the ages of 20 nurses and their heights (in centimetres).

nurse	A	B	C	D	E	F	G	H	I	J
age	23	32	41	25	26	45	33	49	38	20
height	155	160	160	165	165	175	165	160	165	150

nurse	K	L	M	N	O	P	Q	R	S	T
age	36	36	30	43	50	28	35	46	40	21
height	160	155	170	155	155	160	150	150	165	160

a Draw a scatter diagram.
Start your horizontal axis at 20 and use a scale of 2 cm = 5 years.
Start your vertical axis at 140 cm and use a scale of 2 cm = 10 cm (of height).
b Comment on any correlation indicated in the scatter diagram.

6 This table records the heights of a group of 20 adults (in centimetres) and their weights (in kilograms).

adult	A	B	C	D	E	F	G	H	I	J
height	160	170	155	175	165	185	175	160	180	170
weight	43	60	45	65	54	70	60	50	73	57

adult	K	L	M	N	O	P	Q	R	S	T
height	155	165	180	170	180	155	165	175	185	160
weight	40	51	69	52	63	38	45	63	81	45

a Draw a scatter diagram.
Start your horizontal axis at 140 cm and use a scale of 2 cm = 10 cm (of height).
Start your vertical axis at 20 kg and use a scale of 2 cm = 10 kg.
b Comment on any correlation indicated in the scatter diagram.

Line of best fit

If two variables are perfectly correlated then all the points in a scatter diagram will lie on the same line.
This scatter diagram shows the correlation between the diameter and circumference of twenty circles.

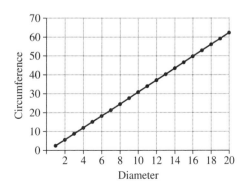

Because circumference and diameter are perfectly correlated, all the points lie on the same straight line.

If a scatter diagram indicates that two variables are highly correlated we can add *a line of best fit*. This is the line closest to a straight line which would connect all the points if the variables were perfectly correlated.

Example 3

This table shows the ages of 10 children and their times to run 100 m.

child	A	B	C	D	E	F	G	H	I	J
age	8	4	11	8	6	7	5	4	9	10
time (seconds)	17	23	14	15	20	20	22	26	15	16

a Draw a scatter diagram and add the line of best fit.
b Estimate the time a child of 8 years and 6 months would take to run 100 m.

a We draw the scatter diagram and then, using a transparent ruler, judge by eye the position of the line of best fit, balancing points above the line with points below the line.

Here is the scatter diagram with a line of best fit added.

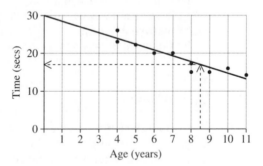

b The line drawn up from the age axis to the line of best fit and across to the time axis allows us to estimate that a child of 8 years 6 months will run 100 m in about 17 seconds.

Exercise 9.2

1 This scatter graph shows the correlation between the engine capacity (in cubic centimetres) and the urban fuel consumption (in miles per gallon) of a group of cars.
A line of best fit has been added to the scatter diagram.

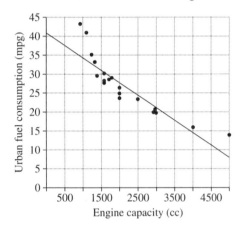

a Comment on any correlation indicated in the scatter diagram.
b Estimate the urban fuel consumption of cars with engine capacities of
  (i) 2000 cc   (ii) 3500 cc   (iii) 4500 cc   (iv) 1000 cc
c Estimate the engine capacity of a car with an urban fuel consumption of
  (i) 30 mpg   (ii) 10 mpg   (iii) 25 mpg

2 This scatter graph shows the correlation between the engine capacity (in cubic centimetres) and the top speed (in miles per hour) of a group of cars.
A line of best fit has been added to the scatter diagram.

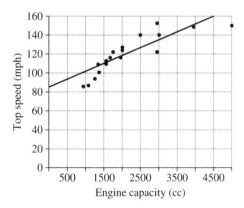

a Comment on any correlation indicated in the scatter diagram.
b Estimate the top speed of cars with engine capacities of
  (i) 2000 cc   (ii) 3500 cc   (iii) 4500 cc   (iv) 1000 cc
c Estimate the engine capacity of a car with a top speed of
  (i) 100 mph   (ii) 130 mph   (iii) 90 mph   (iv) 110 mph

3 A science student measures the current (in amps) that flows through a circuit as the voltage is increased from 0 volts to 100 volts.

voltage	0	10	20	30	40	50	60	70	80	90	100
current	0.0	1.1	1.8	3.2	3.7	5.3	6.2	6.8	8.1	9.3	10.0

a Draw a scatter diagram on 2 mm graph paper.
Plot the voltage on the horizontal axis using a scale of 2 cm = 20 volts.
Plot the current on the vertical axis, using a scale of 2 cm = 1 amp.
b Comment on any correlation indicated in the scatter diagram.
c Add a line of best fit the scatter diagram.
d Estimate the current that will flow through the circuit if the voltage is
    (i) 25 volts   (ii) 55 volts   (iii) 75 volts   (iv) 15 volts
e Estimate the voltage if the current which flows through the circuit is
    (i) 0.5 amps   (ii) 3.5 amps   (iii) 6.5 amps   (iv) 8.7 amps

4 A group of students have holiday jobs in a factory. They complete a survey linking the number of hours they worked each week with the number of hours they spent watching television.

hours worked	15	15	20	20	20	25	25	30	30	30
hours watching TV	30	34	35	30	32	29	25	28	26	25

hours worked	30	35	35	35	35	35	40	40	45	50
hours watching TV	22	18	20	22	15	21	20	18	15	12

a Draw a scatter diagram on 2 mm graph paper.
Plot the hours worked on the horizontal axis using a scale of 2 cm = 5 hours.
Plot the hours watching television on the vertical axis, using a scale of 2 cm = 5 hours.
b Comment on any correlation indicated in the scatter diagram.
c Add a line of best fit the scatter diagram.
d Estimate the time spent watching television by a student who works
    (i) 22 hours   (ii) 27 hours   (iii) 36 hours   (iv) 43 hours
e Estimate the hours worked by a student who watches television for
    (i) 22 hours   (ii) 27 hours

5 A horticultural scientist measures the water used on 10 trial plots of seedlings and the average growth of the seedlings. These are her results.

water used (thousand litres)	1	1	2	2	3	3	4	4	5	5
average growth (cm)	3.2	2.7	3.8	3.5	5.2	4.5	6.7	5.0	6.0	6.9

a Draw a scatter diagram on 2 mm graph paper.
Plot the water used on the horizontal axis using a scale of 2 cm = 1 thousand litres.
Plot the average growth on the vertical axis, using a scale of 2 cm = 1 cm (of growth).
b Comment on any correlation indicated in the scatter diagram.
c Add a line of best fit to the scatter diagram.
d Estimate the average growth of a plot of seedlings watered with
  (i) 1.5 thousand litres   (ii) 3.5 thousand litres
  (iii) 6 thousand litres   (iv) 0.5 thousand litres
e Estimate the water used on a plot of seedlings with an average growth of
  (i) 2 cm   (ii) 6.5 cm   (iii) 4.5 cm   (iv) 6 cm

6 A science student is investigating the correlation between the length of a pendulum and the time it takes to complete one swing. She suspects there is a correlation between the square root of the pendulum length and the time.

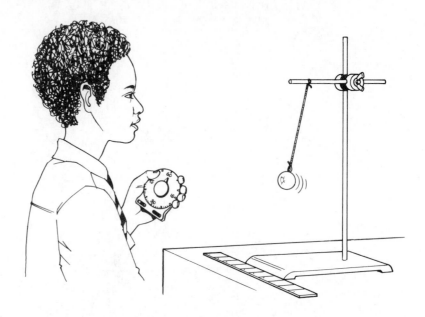

This is her table of results.

length (cm)	10	20	30	40	50	60	70	80	90	100
square root of length (1 dp)	3.2	4.5	5.5	6.3	7.0	7.7	8.4	8.9	9.5	10
time (sec)	0.5	0.9	1.1	1.2	1.4	1.5	1.7	1.7	1.8	2.0

a Draw a scatter diagram on 2 mm graph paper.
   Plot the square root of the length on the horizontal axis, using a scale of 2 cm = 1 unit.
   Plot the time on the vertical axis, using a scale of 4 cm = 1 second.
b Comment on any correlation indicated in the scatter diagram.
c Add a line of best fit to the scatter diagram.
d Estimate the time of a single swing for a pendulum with a length of
   (i) 36 cm   (ii) 49 cm   (iii) 64 cm   (iv) 81 cm
e Estimate the length of a pendulum with a time for one swing of
   (i) 1 second   (ii) 1.6 seconds.